BOTANY

LECTURES HANDBOOK

DWIGHT G. SMITH ✿ DAVID F. AVERY

MARCIA SCHULTZ, EDITOR

PEARSON

Custom Publishing

Cover photo courtesy of PhotoDisc.

Printed in the United States of America

10 9 8 7 6 5 4 3 2 1

ISBN 0-536-96503-X

2005140170

BK/NR

Please visit our web site at *www.pearsoncustom.com*

PEARSON CUSTOM PUBLISHING
75 Arlington Street, Suite 300, Boston, MA 02116
A Pearson Education Company

Table of Contents

Chapter 1   A Science called Botany   1
Chapter 2   Chemistry of Life   10
Chapter 3   Plant Cells and Their Functions   18
Chapter 4   Plant Tissues   30
Chapter 5   Plant Stems   37
Chapter 6   Plant Roots   47
Chapter 7   Plant Leaves   53
Chapter 8   Flowers, Fruits, and Seeds   60
Chapter 9   Water, Minerals, and Soils   71
Chapter 10   Photosynthesis and Respiration   78
Chapter 11   Plant Growth   86
Chapter 12   Meiosis and Life Cycles of Plants   93
Chapter 13   Genetics and Plant Breeding   98
Chapter 14   Plant Evolution   103
Chapter 15   Plant Taxonomy   111
Chapter 16   Plant Ecology   115
Chapter 17   Kingdom Monera: Viruses and Bacteria   119
Chapter 18   Kingdom Protista: The Algae   128
Chapter 19   The Fungi and Lichens   140
Chapter 20   Nonvascular Plants: The Bryophytes   151
Chapter 21   The Ferns and Fern Relatives   158
Chapter 22   The Gymnosperms   166
Chapter 23   The Flowering Plants   172
Chapter 24   Foods and Medicines from Plants   186

An Introduction to *Botany Lectures Handbook*

A. Introduction and Scope

This book is designed as a review of the basic concepts and information about the science of botany. This book closely follows the botany textbook, by authors Avery & Smith. Students may chose to review chapters before and after classroom lectures about the topic. This book also provides a review of key concepts and taxonomy prior to tests. However, *Botany Lectures Handbook* should not be used as a substitute for the textbook or lab manual. We strongly encourage a frequent reading of both.

B. Format of The *Botany Lectures Handbook*

Throughout *Botany Lectures Handbook* is presented in outline format. All basic concepts and information about plants are presented in a step by step fashion and format. For many students, remembering the taxonomy and characteristics of the major plant groups is very challenging. Recognizing this, we have presented each group as a separate chapter in which the basic characteristics of the group are carefully enumerated along with life cycles of typical species within the group.

C. Using the *Botany Lectures Handbook*

For maximum benefit, plan to read the appropriate chapters in *Botany Lectures Handbook* before each lecture and before reading each chapter in the textbook. The chapters in this review book provides a step by step approach to the body of information known as plant science or botany. Therefore, a rereading of the book prior to each test should prove beneficial. Nevertheless, *Botany Lectures Handbook* should not be used as a substitute for reading the textbook, which itself contains an enormous amount of scientific content. Instead, this book should be used as a guidebook to subjects covered in the textbook.

D. Preparing for Tests

Preparing for lecture and laboratory tests should begin immediately following classroom time. We suggest that preparations for each lecture test should include the following:
   a. Read the assigned textbook chapters carefully.
   b. Complete the practice tests in the workbook at the end of the textbook.
   c. Review the chapters in *Botany Lectures Handbook* to ensure that you are
       familiar with concepts and information covered in the appropriate
       chapters of the textbook and lab manual.

E. Answers to Self-Quizzes

At the end of each review chapter we have prepared a series of self-test exercises. Answers to the self-test questions may be found in the textbook or lab manual, both of which should be treated as fundamental resources for the botany course.

Chapter *1* A Science Called Botany

This Chapter Considers the Following Questions

➢ What are plants?
➢ How are plants related to animals and other kinds of life?
➢ Why are plants ecologically important?
➢ How did botany become a science?
➢ What is the importance of botany as a science?
➢ What are some of the current studies and problems in botany?
➢ What are the characteristics of living plants?

I Comparing Plants with other types of Life on Earth

A. Bacteria were the earliest forms of life.

1. Bacteria ruled the earth for about a billion years. There were no other forms of life on earth, although viruses may have been present. Then, as now, the forms of bacteria were abundant in the soil, water, and air.
2. Bacteria are simple, single-celled or colonial forms that lack a nucleus.
3. All other forms of life, protistans, fungi, plants, and animals, evolved from bacteria.
4. The study of botany traditionally includes the true plants as well as protistans, fungi, bacteria, and viruses. Fungi, bacteria, and viruses are not plants, however.
5. Protistans are immediate ancestors of true plants.

B. Defining Plants or What Makes a Plant a Plant?

1. Plants are living organisms that manufacture their own food by the process of photosynthesis. Some modern plants do not manufacture their own food, but have evolved from ancestors that did. These are parasitic plants.
2. Plants differ from animals in several ways:
    (a) plant cells are surrounded by a cell wall
    (b) plants manufacture their own food photosynthetically
    (c) most plants have limited mobility or entirely lack mobility.
    (d) plants lack a nervous system
    (e) plants respond slowly to environmental stimuli
    (f) plants store food in storage vacuoles in cells
    (g) plants absorb nutrients directly from the environment and convert it into plant tissue

II The Science of Botany

A. The Study of Plants is Called Botany
1. Botany is the scientific study of:
   (a) the diversity and relationships of plants
   (b) the anatomy and organization of plants
   (c) the structure and function of plants
   (d) the ecology and evolution of plants

B. Botany is one of the Biological Sciences
1. The other kinds of biological sciences include zoology and microbiology.
2. Paleontology, the study of ancient life is also sometimes included in the life sciences.
3. To contrast botany with zoology-zoology is the study of animals such as sponges, jellyfish, flatworms, roundworms, segmented worms, insects, lobsters, and the vertebrates including fish, amphibians, reptiles, and mammals. The last also includes humans.
4. Microbiology is the science that studies microorganisms such as bacteria. The study of viruses is included in microbiology courses. Bacteria and viruses are also studied in botany.

III. The Importance of Plants

A. Plants Produce Energy in all of the World's Ecosystems.
1. Plants are called producers because they convert sunlight into plant biomass.
2. This plant biomass becomes food not only for plants but for all animals.

B. Plants as Decomposers
1. Ecologically plants like some of the fungi and bacteria are important within ecosystems because they break down (decompose) dead organic matter, converting it back into minerals.
2. These organisms are collectively called decomposers.
3. Without plants as decomposers, all nutrients would soon be tied up (chemically bound) in the dead bodies of plants and animals and therefore be unavailable for new life.

C. Plant Products are used by Humans
1. Foods such as vegetables, grains, and spices are plant products.
2. Food dyes, fiber, stabilizers, and emulsifiers are plant products.
3. Many types of dyes and adhesives are plant products.
4. Plants are primary source of many building materials such as lumber, resins, hemp, fibers, turpentine.

5. Paper, cardboard, and most packing materials are plant products.
6. Plant fibers from cotton plants are used for clothing.
7. Plants are the only source of many vitamins and drugs.
8. Plants are important sources of fossil fuels such as coal and oil. Coal and oil are hydrocarbon residues of plants and bacteria that existed millions of years ago, which were transformed over geological time into our primary fuel sources.
9. Currently, plants are important producers of energy substances such as gasohol, a type of gasoline derived from plant biomass.

D. Plants are the Oxygen Generators of the World

1. Almost all of the atmospheric oxygen, which now comprises some 21% of atmospheric gases, has originated from the oxygen released during plant photosynthesis.
2. Since aerobic (oxygen breathing) animals (as well as plants) require oxygen, without plants animals would die.

IV. Botany as a Science
A. Botany Explores and Evaluates the Environment of Plants.

1. Botany comes from the French word *botanique* and Greek words *botanikos* (botanica), *botane* (plant or herd) and *boskein* (to feed).
2. Originally the need to know botany grew out of the need to plant food. Botany later developed into systematic collection of knowledge and formalized study.
3. Botany very early became a major science of ancient peoples. Most monoliths of the world such as Stonehenge were constructed as solar calendars that provided key information needed to know when to plant crops and when to harvest crops.

B. Botany, like other sciences, is based on the Scientific Method

1. A systematic way of looking at information that includes observation, verification of observations, and discarding useless information.
2. Science is defined as the search for truth and knowledge through observation, hypothesis making, experimentation, and the setting forth of theories that explain the initial observations.
3. The **inductive reasoning** method is building theories and hypotheses based on observations.
4. The **deductive reasoning** method begins by forming a theory about an event, then obtaining observations and determining whether they support the theory or not.
5. The methodology of science consists of four basic components:
   a. **Observation**- a scientist observes a phenomena that needs explaining

b. **Hypothesis**---is a tentative, unproven explanation for something observed.

c. **Experimentation**---botanists collect data by conducting experiments.

d. **Theory**-Botanists analyze the collected data to develop a theory that seems to fit the observations.

6. Observations are the collections of facts gathered in an experiment.

7. Hypotheses are educated guesses which provide one or more possible explanations for the observations. Hypotheses follow observations and are shaped by observations.

8. In experimentation, hypotheses are tested using rigorous scientific protocol (methods) to determine how correctly they fit the observation. That is, how well they provide an explanation that satisfactorily explains the observations.

9. A theory is an explanation of a problem based on data gathered by experimentation and has a high probably of being correct.

10. A scientific law is a theory that has been proven beyond all reasonable doubt.

C. Pure and Applied Botanical Science

1. Pure science is about basic research. It is often based entirely on thinking and thought processes. Experiments are constructed in the mind and possible explanations are evaluated. All of this takes place prior to testing and actual experimentation.

2. Applied science is the application of the results of pure science. Some of the many examples of applied science include fisheries management, agriculture, and animal husbandry.

3. Plants are important for research in genetic engineering, where genes are implanted in certain species to produce substances that humans need. Because plants are common and relatively easy to work with, much of the current emphasis on genetic engineering is focused on plants rather than animals.

V. The History of Botany as a Science
A. Humans have always observed the plants around them.

1. For thousands and millions of years, the survival of our ancestors depended on their knowledge of which plants provided food and medicines and which plants did not.

2. The earliest people recognized and used many species of plants for food and medicines.

3. Primitive people started to cultivate plants between 35,000-15,000 years ago. Cultivation became increasingly important after the great herds of mammals that covered most of the northern half of the world were depleted by human hunters, forcing us to seek a different food source.

4. The growth of cultivation and farming was well established between 13,000 to 9,000 BC.
5. By 8,000 BC agriculture was well established in many of the warmer parts of the world, especially in southeast Asia, the near East, and southern Africa.
6. In the Middle East, a variety of grains, fruits, figs, olives, and dates were cultivated.
7. By 2,737 BC, the Chinese had invented the plow and invoked a seed-sowing ceremony.
8. From about 5,000-3,400 and possibly earlier, the Egyptians cultivated wheat and barley--- by the fifth century BC the Egyptians were making beer from barley and other farm products.

B. The Science of Botany was first studied in Ancient Greece.

1. The Greeks maintained a practical interest in plants as well as food and drugs. Ancient doctors and pharmacists recognized many kinds as useful.
2. Aristotle 322 BC, student of Plato, philosopher and scientist, created a botanical garden in Athens and wrote extensively about plants.
3. Theophrastus was Aristotle's successor. He wrote over 200 papers on botany and is considered to be the father of botany.

C. The first books about plants were called Herbals.

1. The first Herbals were written during the 2nd century AD when the Roman Empire was at its zenith.
2. Herbals were written accounts of plants that provided drugs and other medicinal remedies that could be used for food as well as spices.
3. Herbals were tremendously important as a main source of information about plants during the Dark Ages (Middle Ages). Many herbals were published after 1400 and the period from 1500-1700 is called Age of Herbals.
4. Most herbalists were German, but Italian and English botanists also published herbal accounts of medicinal plants.

D. The Doctrine of Signatures appeared in the Middle Ages.

1. This school of botanists claimed that if a part of a plant was shaped like part of the human body then that plant would be useful for treatment of disease. For example, since kidney beans look like kidneys, eating kidney beans would eliminate ailments of the human kidney.

E. Modern Botany and Agriculture

1. Modern agriculture began in the early 1600's with widespread introduction of New World Crops into the Old World. Examples include potatoes, corn and tomatoes, which were brought back to Europe by the early English and Spanish explorers.

2. Following World War II, a concerted effort on part of scientists in world-wide research institutes such as IRRI (International Rice Research Institute) resulted in development of new high yielding varieties of rice, wheat, and corn. Called the **Green Revolution**, this did much to alleviate food shortages in the world.

F. Botany in the 21st Century

1. Plant science promises great future for humans. Among the topics of particular interest were discovery of new species, hybrid varieties for food, clothing, medicines, and identification of endangered habitats such as tropical rain forests.
2. Perhaps 1/3 of all plants, possibly more, await discovery. Most of the undiscovered plants are species of algae and fungi.
3. Tropical rain forests are endangered and there is a race to save those that are remaining. Furthermore, discovery of new plant species may prove useful as sources of food and medicines.

VI. What Botanists Study

1. Plant Anatomy--- the study of internal and external structures of plants.
2. Plant Physiology---the study of how plants function.
3. Plant Taxonomy---the study of identifying, naming and classifying plants.
4. Plant Ecology---the study of how plants interact with one another and with their environment.
5. Plant Morphology---the study of the structure and function of plants.
6. Plant Genetics---the study of heredity, of plant genes and hybridization.

VII. The Characteristics of Life

A. All life is descended from a single ancestor that originated at some remote period some 3.6-3.8 billion years ago. Therefore, all living organisms have several features in common. These are called the characteristics of life.

1. A Unique Chemistry. All organisms share a unique chemistry based on organic chemicals such as carbohydrates, lipids, proteins, and nucleic acids. This organic chemistry is manufactured by organisms themselves, which extract raw materials from nature and use them to synthesize these organic chemicals with the help of enzymes. In fact, organic chemistry takes its name from organisms.
2. DNA Genetic Material. As part of their unique chemistry, all plants and all other organisms share the same basic genetic material called DNA. Organisms differ only in the chemical blueprints contained within the DNA molecule of heredity.

3. Growth. All organisms have the ability to extract nutrients such as water and minerals from the environment and chemically convert them into biomass for growth and reproduction.

4. Metabolism. The process of synthesizing energy and biomass from raw materials is called metabolism. Only organisms have the ability to extract needed nutrients from their environment and convert them into new organic chemicals.

5. Reproduction. Life does not originate from spontaneous generation, but comes from reproduction of preexisting life.

6. Movement. All organisms are capable of movement in response to stimuli. Movement in plants is less obvious than in animals.

7. Evolution. Is the genetic adaptation of organisms to their environment. Short term adaptation to stimuli is called irritability.

Self-Test Multiple-Choice

_____ 1. A life science that studies animals rather than plants is called: (a) biology (b) zoology (c) paleontology (d) all of the above (e) none of the above.

_____ 2. Short term response to environmental stimuli is termed: (a) evolution (b) reproduction (c) metabolism (d) irritability (e) all of the above.

_____ 3. These best-selling books of the Middle Ages were popular pharmacopias: (a) Herbalists (b) Herbals (c) textbooks (d) novels.

_____ 4. The earliest forms of life on earth were: (a) animals (b) plants (c) fungi (d) bacteria (e) humans (f) all of the above.

_____ 5. Designing an experiment to explain an observed event is called: (a) theory (b) deductive method (c) inductive method (d) observation.

_____ 6. Which is not found in plants? (a) cells (b) cell walls (c) nervous system (d) adaptation to environment (e) mobility (f) nutrient acquisition.

_____ 7. In the scientific method the experiment comes after the: (a) theory (b) question (c) hypothesis (d) observation (e) all of the above.

Self Test Matching

_____ 1. Short-term response to environment		a. evolution
_____ 2. Long term adaptation to environment		b. metabolism
_____ 3. Genetic material of life		c. DNA
_____ 4. Synthesis of plant flesh from nonliving nutrients		d. growth
_____ 5. Making new plants		e. reproduction
_____ 6. Dispersal, transfer of materials within plant s		f. movement

Some Key Terms

Herbals	observation	zoology
Doctrine of Signatures	theory	paleontology
Theophrastus	metabolism	decomposers
Pharmacopoeia	bacteria	inductive
Hypothesis	fungi	deductive
Boskein	experiment	Aristotle
Green Revolution	fungi	protistans

Test Your Visual Understanding

Picture source: Jim Harter. Animals. Dover Press.

The vintage Victorian print at left illustrates some of the differences between animals (in this case birds called macaws) and plants of the tropical rain forest. Write in some of the obvious differences between the two major groups in the spaces.

	Animals	**Plants**
Form		
Movement		
Food		
Reproduction		
Growth		
Senses		
Response Rate		

Concepts Self-Test

1. Is botany a pure science or an applied science or both? In developing your answer to this question, list and briefly describe examples of concerns about plants, self interest in plants, and applications of plant science that have local, regional, and global consequences.

2. Scientists often speak of the unity and diversity of life. Take a sheet of paper and make three columns. Label the first column factor, the second column unity, and the third column diversity. In the first column make a list of common life characteristics such as DNA, organic chemistry, and so forth. In the next two columns, describe how each of these factors might be unifying but also different with respect to the great variety of organisms that occur on earth.

Chapter 2 **Chemistry of Life**

This chapter considers the following questions:
  ➤ What is atomic structure?
  ➤ What are molecules and compounds?
  ➤ What processes occur in chemical bonding?
  ➤ What are acids, bases, salts, and pH?
  ➤ What are the types of chemical reactions?
  ➤ How are carbohydrates, lipids, proteins, and nucleic acids
        a part of living organisms?

I. The Chemical Properties of Life
  1. Life is made up of chemical matter and energy. The two are interchangeable: that is matter = energy and energy = matter.
  2. Matter is energy contained in a structure. Matter can be converted into energy.
  3. Energy is randomized matter in motion. Slow the motion and matter forms.
  4. Both matter and energy obey physical and chemical laws of nature.

II. Some Basic Chemistry
  1. All life and other substances are made up of elements. An element is anything which has mass and takes up space. There are 92 naturally occurring elements. Examples of elements include gold, silver, hydrogen, oxygen, nitrogen, phosphorous, and carbon.
  2. The fundamental unit of all elements are atoms. Atoms of elements differ in several ways.
  3. At least 24-26 elements occur naturally in animals including carbon, hydrogen, oxygen, nitrogen, calcium, phosphorous, sulfur, magnesium, iodine, copper, sodium, and iron.

A. Atomic Structure
  1. Atoms are the basic building blocks of nature because all substances are comprised of atoms.
  2. Each atom is made up of one or more protons, neutrons, and electrons.
  3. The nucleus is the central mass of the atom that is positively charged.
      (a) the nucleus contains protons and neutrons.
      (b) the nucleus is surrounded by a cloud of one or more electrons.
  4. Protons have a positive charge and always occur in the nucleus.
  5. Neutrons are similar in mass to protons, but have a neutral charge.
  6. Electrons have a negative charge and occur in a series of orbits or energy shells around the nucleus.

7. The atomic number of an element depends on the number of protons making up each atom of a particular element. For example, carbon has 6 protons in its nucleus---therefore the atomic number is 6. Normal atoms of carbon also have 6 neutrons.

8. The atomic mass of an element is the sum of its protons, neutrons and electrons.

9. Isotopes are atoms that do not have the same number of neutrons. For example, the different isotopes of uranium as U^{235} and U^{238} have the same number of protons but differ in the number of neutrons that they have.

10. A molecule is made up of two or more atoms chemically bonded together. Molecular nitrogen, for example, is comprised of three nitrogen molecules chemically bonded together.

11. Compounds are comprised of two or more molecules. Sucrose is an example of a compound.

B. Chemical Bonding

1. The number of electrons in the outer energy shell of an atom determines its chemical stability (whether it will readily enter into reactions) and activity.

2. An electron donor is an atom that donates electrons to another atom. It is called a metal.

3. An electron acceptor is a non-metal that accepts electrons from another atom.

4. The number of electrons in the outer energy shell of an atom also determines the electrical charge or oxidation number of the atom.

5. Electromagnetic forces that hold atoms together in molecules are called chemical bonds.

6. The strongest type of chemical bond is ionic bonds. In ionic bonds, one atom donates electrons to another atom. Their resulting electrical charges "cement" them together.

7. Oxidation reactions occur when an atom loses one or more electrons while reduction reactions occur when an atom gains electrons.

8. Covalent bonds share electrons between bonded atoms. Most organic molecules are held together by covalent bonds, which are the most common type of chemical bond in life.

9. Hydrogen bonds are chemical bonds in organic elements between adjacent hydrogen atoms.

10. Disulfide bonds are chemical bonds between hydrocarbon atoms and sulfur or between sulfur atoms. Metallic bonds share electrons.

C. Acids, Bases, Salt and pH

1. An acid is any chemical substance that releases hydrogen ions (H^+) when it dissolves in water.

2. A base is any substance that releases hydroxyl ions (OH⁻) when dissolved and strong bases dissolve completely or almost completely.

3. A salt is a molecular combination of an acid and a base. Table salt (NaCl) is an example of salt.

4. Plant fluids are classified as acidic, basic or neutral. Most plant fluids are slightly basic but this depends on the type of fluid and its location in the body of the plant. Other factors such as how recently an animal has absorbed nutrients or produced new chemical compounds for growth and metabolic processes are equally important.

5. The degree of acidity or alkalinity of a solution is expressed by the pH of that solution.

6. The pH of fluids is closely maintained by substances called buffers. A buffer can chemically react with an acid or base to neutralize it, or bring it closer to a neutral pH.

D. Types of Chemical Reactions

1. Chemical reactions involve the chemical alteration of atoms and molecules which react together to form different products. The products typically have different chemical properties compared to the original chemicals.

2. In decomposition reactions, larger molecules are broken down into smaller molecules or atoms. An example is the chemical decomposition of sucrose into glucose and fructose.

3. Synthesis reactions or anabolism when it takes place in cells are the opposite of decomposition reactions. An example is the formation of maltose by the chemical bonding of two glucose molecules.

4. Exchange reactions involve two reactants which transfer some of their atoms or molecules to form two products as seen in the reaction: $NaHCO_3 + HCl \rightarrow NaCl + H_2CO_3$

5. Most chemical reactions that occur are reversible.

III Chemistry of Life
A. The Inorganic Chemistry of life

1. The most important inorganic chemicals in living organisms include water, oxygen, carbon dioxide and a variety of inorganic salts, acids and bases.

2. Almost all of the thousands of different chemical reactions that occur in cells take place in water. Water dictates the shape and form of many plant cells. It has a high specific heat capacity which allows it to absorb or give off heat without changing the overall temperature.

3. Water is an excellent lubricant for reducing friction between adjacent surfaces.

4. There are three types of mixtures that involve water as a solvent: solutions, suspensions, and colloid suspensions.

B. The Organic Chemistry of Life

1. The organic chemicals of living organisms are often called hydrocarbons because their primary structure is based on carbon-to-carbon chains to which atoms of hydrogen are bonded.
2. The four kinds of organic chemicals are carbohydrates, lipids (fats), proteins and nucleic acids.

C. Carbohydrates are the most abundant organic compounds in nature.

1. Carbohydrates are comprised of atoms of carbon, hydrogen, and oxygen in the typical ratio of $C^nH^{2n}O^n$. This means that there are 2 atoms of H for every atom of C and O. A common and typical carbohydrate in all plants is glucose with the formula $C_6H_{12}O_6$.
2. There are three types of carbohydrates in plants and other organisms, monosaccharides, disaccharides, and polysaccharides.
   a. Monosaccharides consist of a single sugar molecule. Examples include glucose, fructose, and ribose.
   b. Monosaccharides can chemically combine to form disaccharides, which are comprised of two sugar molecules bonded together. Sucrose is a disaccharide.
   c. Polysaccharides consist of many sugar molecules bonded together. Examples include starch and cellulose. Starch consists of 64-68 glucose molecules and is for energy storage. Cellulose molecules are huge chains of 2000 glucose molecules. Cellulose is the major structural molecule of the plant. Much of what we see when we look at plants is cellulose.

D. Lipids are a class of hydrocarbons that include fats and substances with fat-like properties.

1. Chemically, lipids consist of atoms of carbon, hydrogen, and oxygen. There are usually far more hydrogen molecules. During metabolism, lipids yield far more energy than other organic substances. There are several types of lipids in plants, including triglycerides, phospholipids, and waxes.
2. Phospholipids are lipid molecules that are comprised of a glycerol molecule bonded to two fatty acid molecules plus a phosphate molecule from which they take their name. Phospholipids form the cell membranes of all cells.
3. Waxes are lipid-like substances made up of fatty acids complexed with alcohols. Most waxes are used for water proofing plant surfaces.

E. Proteins are large and complex organic molecules.

1. Proteins are the most important structural and regulatory chemicals of cells. Chemically, they are comprised of atoms of carbon, hydrogen, oxygen,

and nitrogen. Other chemicals in some proteins include sulfur and phosphates.
2. Structurally, proteins are long chains of amino acids. Most are composed of hundreds of amino acids all bonded together by peptide bonds.
3. There are 20 types of amino acids found in plants and each protein is made up of a specific mix of amino acids that are linked together by covalent peptide bonds.
4. Whether large or small in size, all proteins are comprised of all 20 of the different amino acids in their chemical makeup. Their different arrangements promote an enormous variety of molecule shapes and sizes and molecular configurations.
5. Proteins have a complex configuration consisting of a primary, secondary, and tertiary structure.
      a. The primary structure of a protein is the sequence of amino acids along the chain.
      b. The chain (or chains) of amino acids is twisted in a regular or repeated way to form a helix or pleated structure which is called the secondary structure of a protein.
      c. The helix may be twisted on itself to produce a complex configuration called the tertiary structure of a protein.
6. Fibrous proteins are long thread-like strands that are used as structural components of cells and tissues while globular proteins are circular or amorphous in shape.

F. Proteins as Enzymes

1. Of the several types of proteins, some of the most important are enzymes. An enzyme is a protein that catalyzes a specific reaction. All physiological reactions in plants are directed by or catalyzed by enzymes which can cause and promote chemical reactions and may increase the speed of a chemical reaction. Enzymes catalyze reactions but are not changed or altered themselves during the process.
2. Pro-enzymes are precursors of enzymes that are manufactured in an inactive form that must be changed into an active form (often by another enzyme) for the enzyme to function.
3. In enzymes that are made up of a protein and vitamin complex, the vitamin is called a coenzyme. The vitamins are organic molecules manufactured by plants.
4. In enzymes made up of protein and minerals the mineral component is called a cofactor. The minerals in such enzymes are absorbed from the soil and retained within the plant.

G. Nucleic Acids

1. Nucleic acids are chemical repositories of information at the cellular level. Chemically, nucleic acids are comprised of molecules of sugar, phosphate, and nitrogenous bases, all bonded together in long, complex chains. The two major forms of nucleic acids in plants and other organisms are DNA (deoxyribonucleic acid) and RNA (ribonucleic acid).

2. DNA is a molecular structure that represents one form of nucleic acids.

3. RNA is a second molecular structure that represents another form of nucleic acids.

4. Nucleic acids are made up of compounds called nucleotides.

   a. Each nucleotide consists of a molecule of phosphate, a molecule of sugar, and a molecule of nitrogenous base.

   b. Five different molecules of nitrogenous bases are found in nature, adenine, cytosine, guanine, thymine, and uracil.

   c. So one type of nucleotide would consist of a phosphate, sugar, and uracil.

   d. How many different kinds of nucleotides can exist? (Answer 5)

5. Ribose is a form of sugar molecule in nucleic acids. It exists in two forms, deoxyribose and ribose sugars.

   a. Deoxyribose sugar occurs in DNA molecules.

   b. Ribose sugar occurs in RNA molecules.

6. The molecular structure of DNA resembles a spiral staircase. The edges are phosphate atoms and sugar molecules. The "steps" of the ladder-like molecule.

   a. Pairs of nitrogenous bases complete the "rungs" or steps in the staircase.

   b. Pairs are adenine-thymine (A-T) and cytosine –guanine (C-G).

7. The molecular structure of RNA resembles a single strand, or one half of a DNA molecule. RNA also differs from DNA in having the nitrogenous base uracil which substitutes for the nitrogenous base thymine. Thus, RNA has adenine, uracil, cytosine, and guanine bases.

8. DNA and RNA molecules differ in both their structural makeup and in their specific functions within the cell.

   a. DNA comprises the chromosomes. It is the stuff of our genes. The sequence of nitrogenous bases along a strand of DNA molecule spells out a chemical blueprint for the synthesis of protein enzymes.

   b. The chemical blueprint is contained within the sequence of nitrogenous base along the gene segment of the DNA.

Multiple Choice Self-Test

_____ 1. Nucleic acids contain how many bases? (a) one (b) two (c) three (d) four

_____ 2. A common structural carbohydrate in plants is? (a) cellulose (b) cellulite
(c) glucose (d) sucrose (e) starch (f) all of the above.

_____ 3. The basic molecular components of proteins are: (a) nucleotides (b) starch
(c) amino acids (d) polysaccharides (e) all of the above.

_____ 4. Molecules that have a carbon backbone or skeleton are collectively called:
(a) water (b) organic (c) inorganic (d) ionic (e) covalent.

_____ 5. One of the most common molecule in plants is: (a) water (b) proteins
(c) lipids (d) iron (e) hemoglobin.

_____ 6. Which part of an atomic nucleus has mass but no charge? (a) orbit
(b) orbital (c) neutron (d) proton (e) electron.

_____ 7. Which is not part of the nucleus of an atom? (a) electron (b) proton (c) neutron

_____ 8. Neutral pH is: (a) 100 (b) 7 (c) 8 (d) 7.4 (e) all of the above.

_____ 9. A DNA molecule takes the shape or form of: (a) a staircase (b) a helix
(c) a ladder (d) a double helix (e) all of the above.

_____ 10. The chemical blueprint of an enzyme permanently resides in: (a) DNA
(b) tRNA (c) mitochondria (d) ribosome (e) all of the above.

_____ 11. Life is made up of matter and: (a) mass (b) protons (c) energy (d) neutrons
(e) none of the above.

_____ 12. We add the neutrons, protons, and electrons to get the: (a) atomic mass
(b) atomic number (c) atomic symbol (d) element symbol.

_____ 13. An acid releases ___ when dissolved in water: (a) calcium (b) hydrogen
ions (c) hydroxal ions (d) all of the above (e) none of the above.

_____ 14. This polysaccharide is the most common structural component of plants:
(a) starch (b) sucrose (c) cellulose (d) enzymes (e) all of the above.

Matching Self-Test

_____ 1. Sharing of electrons in chemical bonding   a. copper

_____ 2. Acid/base measure is called?   b. ionic

_____ 3. Strongest type of chemical bonding?   c. covalent

_____ 4. Example of an inorganic chemical   d. glucose

_____ 5. Example of an organic chemical?   e. molecule

_____ 6. Fundamental unit of matter?   f. energy

_____ 7. Matter is interchangeable with?   g. pH

_____ 8. Two or more bonded atoms is called a?   h. atom

Visual Understanding Self-Test

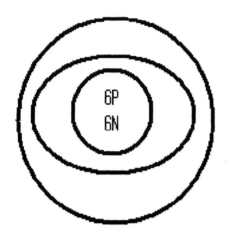

Add the electrons in their orbitals to the diagram on the left. Now, answer the following questions, based on your completed diagram.

_____ 1. Number of protons in this atom?
_____ 2. Number of neutrons in this atom?
_____ 3. Number of electrons in this atom?
_____ 4. Atomic number of this atom?
_____ 5. Approximate atomic mass of this atom?

Concepts Self-Test

1. Put your thinking cap on. Review the base pairings of DNA and the formation of mRNA and tRNA. A strand of three tRNA molecules have the following base sequence: AUCCGUAGC. What was the base sequence of the original mRNA strand that produced this tRNA strand? What was the base sequence of the original DNA strand that produced the mRNA strand?

Chapter 3 Plant Cells and Their Functions

This chapter considers the following questions:

➤ What are plant cells and how were they discovered?
➤ Why are cells central to life and what is the cell principle?
➤ What are the two kinds of cells found in living organisms?
➤ What is the basic structure of cells and the functions of these structures?
➤ What is the role of the cell nucleus?
➤ How do cells reproduce exact copies of themselves?

I. Cells and Cell Study
A. Cells are the Basic Units of Life
    1. All life is made up of cells. That is, all living organisms are comprised of cells and substances manufactured by cells.
    2. The fact that all life is comprised of cells is called the **cell principle.** The cell principle was first proposed by two early microscopists, Matthias Schleiden and Theodor Schwann.
    3. Cells are also the basic functional level of life. That is, all metabolic activities associated with life occur within cells.
    4. The study of the structure and function of cells is called **cytology** or cell biology. Cytology continues to be an important field of plant biology.

B. Plant cells are studied with microscopes
    1. The earliest cells were discovered by the very first microscopists who used microscopes with a single magnifying lens to see cells and cell structures for the first time.
    2. English scientist Robert Hooke was the first to name cells. He studied the cells in the bark of a cork oak tree and noticed grid-like partitions separating small spaces. Hooke called the spaces "cells" because they reminded him of the small cells in which monks lived.

C. Two Types of Cells
    1. Two types of cells are found in nature, **prokaryotic cells** and **eukaryotic cells**.
    2. Prokaryotic cells are found in bacteria and blue-green bacteria (the cyanobacteria).

a. Prokaryotic cells are more primitive than eukaryotic cells. They lack a nucleus to house the DNA. Instead, the DNA occurs in a coiled or ring-shaped strand called a nucleoid, which is attached to the cell membrane or the cell wall.

b. Prokaryotic cells are smaller (less than 5 microns) than eukaryotic cells and have fewer types of cell organelles.

3. Eukaryotic cells have a centrally located nucleus that contains the DNA, packaged in the form of chromosomes visible when the cell is replicating.

a. The organized nucleus and its DNA are the "headquarters" of eukaryotic cells. The nucleus directs cell activities and also serves as a storage repository for the genetic information.

b. Eukaryotic cells are found in plants, fungi, and animals.

II. Basic Cell Structure
A. The Cell Wall of the Plant

1. A typical plant cell is bounded and protected by a cell wall.

2. The cell wall is a semi-rigid structure that provides the framework, shape, strength, and support for the cell. It consists of a **primary cell wall**, a **middle lamella**, and often a **secondary cell wall**.

3. Among eukaryotic organisms, cell walls occur in plants and fungi. They are absent in animals.

4. Cell walls of plants are typically comprised mostly of cellulose along with lesser amounts of lignin, lipids, and pectin.

a. Rows of cellulose are grouped together in bundles called microfibrils that twist together to form rope-like structures called macrofibrils. These extend through a matrix of lipids and lignin much like steel rods run through concrete to give it added strength.

b. Lignin is another large and complex polysaccharide that provides added strength, disease and rot resistance to the cell wall. It is important in the secondary growth of woody plants.

c. Pectin is a complex carbohydrate-lipid-alcohol molecule which cements the different layers of the cell wall.

d. Lipids in the cell wall may include waxes, cutin, and suberin. Cell wall lipids such as waxes help protect and waterproof the cell and also direct water movement.

5. The primary cell wall forms first. The primary cell wall is laid down in layers on the outside of the cell membrane by the action of enzymes manufactured within the enzyme.

6. A middle lamella is formed between the two primary walls of adjacent cells. It consists of a matrix of pectin which acts to cement the adjacent cells together.

7. When cell growth ceases at cell maturity, a protective secondary wall may also be formed inside the primary cell wall. Secondary walls are comprised of cellulose fibers arranged in parallel and impregnated with lignin which strengthens and hardens the plant surfaces. This secondary cell wall is hard and protective and it is also a major ingredient in wood.

8. Cell walls between adjacent cells are often perforated by **plasmodesmata,** which are miniature tubes that conduct fluids and dissolved substances from one cell to another. The plasmodesmata also allow adjacent cells to "communicate" with one another.

B. The Protoplasm

1. The living material of cells is called protoplasm. It includes the cell membrane and all internal cell structures including the cytoplasm and nucleoplasm.

2. The name protoplasm means proto= first and plasm= viscous fluid mix.

C. The Cell Membrane of the Plant

1. Plant cells are bounded by a cell membrane which encloses and protects the cell contents.

2. The cell membrane is comprised of two layers of phospholipids which are termed a **bi-lipid layer** or bipolar layer. The cell membrane also contains some carbohydrates for strength and proteins that function in transport of materials into and out of the cell.

3. The basic functions of the cell membrane are to protect the cell interior and contents and regulate flow of water, minerals, and substances into and out of the cell.

4. Cell membranes of almost all plant cells are semi permeable. Thus, they allow the flow of some substances into and out of the cells. Other possible kinds of membranes are impermeable which prohibit any type of movement, or permeable, which allows free movement of almost all substances between the cell and its environment.

5. Carrier proteins are membrane molecules that bind with chemical substances to facilitate their transport through the cell membrane. Carrier proteins are usually substance-specific. That is, they are chemically complex only with specific substances.

6. Cell membranes regulate the movement of substances and, therefore the chemical composition of cells. There are several methods of movement of materials across cell membranes including diffusion, osmosis, facilitated diffusion, and endocytosis.

a. **Diffusion** is the movement of a substance from an area of greater concentration to an area of lesser concentration. Most minerals and gases move through the cell membrane by simple diffusion through pores in the cell membrane.

b. The **diffusion** of water through a membrane is called osmosis.

c. In **facilitated diffusion,** substances are carried by transport proteins across the membrane following a concentration gradient. This is also called mediated diffusion. The carrier protein is the mediator.

d. **Active transport** is the transportation of substances through a cell membrane by means of a transporter or mediator protein against a concentration gradient. Active transport differs from facilitated diffusion in that energy is consumed. Active transport is used by cells to horde extra supplies of a needed nutrient or nutrients.

e. **Endocytosis** is the transport of large substances into the cell by invagination of the cell membrane around the substance. A segment of the membrane pinches off and surrounds the imported substance, forming a food vacuole.

f. **Exocytosis** is the opposite of endocytosis, that is, exocytosis is the transport of materials out of the cell.

D. The Cytoplasm

1. Cytoplasm is the fluid-filled part of the cell that lies between the nucleus and the cell membrane. It is mostly comprised of water which dissolves minerals, organic substances (amino acids and fatty acids) and organelles.
2. Most of the cytoplasm looks like a clear fluid known as cytosol. Many metabolic reactions take place within the cytosol.
3. The larger structures found in cytoplasm are organelles such as the mitochondria and Golgi bodies. Each organelle performs one or more metabolic functions at the cellular level.

E. Plant Cell Organelles

1. There are several kinds of organelles found in the cytoplasm of most plant cells. The major cytoplasmic organelles include mitochondria, endoplasmic reticulum, ribosomes, Golgi bodies, lysosomes, and chloroplasts.

2. **Mitochondria** are cigar-shaped organelles that are the sites of cell energy production. This process is also called cellular respiration. Mitochondria are bounded and protected by a double-unit (two layers) membrane. The inner membrane is convoluted to invaginations called cristae which hold the many enzymes involved in respiration. Mitochondria produce energy for the cell in form of a high-energy molecule called ATP. This ATP molecule provides the energy that powers all of the cell's activities.

3. The **endoplasmic reticulum** (ER) consists of an extensive network of membranes that extend from the nucleus into the cytoplasm. This series of internal cell membranes forms a conduit for movement of certain substances through the cytoplasm. Some of the ER bears small granules which are actually a separate organelle called ribosomes. ER with ribosomes is called rough ER. Other ER in the cell lacks ribosomes and is called smooth ER which forms a tubular conduit for transporting substances through the cell interior.

4. **Ribosomes** are small globular organelles where proteins and parts of proteins are synthesized. Some ribosomes line the rough ER and also occur freely in the cytoplasm as polysomes. Ribosomes synthesize proteins by "reading" the chemical instructions supplied by genes in the form of messenger RNA molecules.

5. **Golgi bodies** are also called dictyosomes. A cell may contain several hundred, often occurring in clumps of 5-30.

      a. The Golgi apparatus are the collecting, assembly and packaging sites of cells.

      b. Products may include complex carbohydrates, proteins, and phospholipids.

      c. Some products are released as secretory vesicles for export or for transport within the cell itself.

6. **Plastids** are double-membrane bounded organelles that occur in several forms in plant cells. Examples of plastids include chloroplasts, leucoplasts, and chromoplasts. Plastids may convert from one form to another; e.g., leucoplasts transform into chromoplasts when exposed to sunlight; chloroplasts in green tomatoes transform into red pigment-containing chromoplasts when the tomato becomes ripe.

      a. **Chloroplasts** are the most conspicuous group of plastids.

          1) They occur in many shapes from corkscrew ribbons to spindle-shaped to bracelet-shapes. Most are discoidal (like two Frisbees stuck together).

          2) Chloroplasts are numerous in most cells, numbering from 75-125 per cell.

          3) Each chloroplasts has its own ring-shaped DNA molecule that encodes enzymes of photosynthesis.

4) Structurally, each chloroplast consists of three components: **stroma**, **grana** and **thylakoids**.
   (i) the stroma is the liquid substance in which carbon is fixed.
   (ii) thylakoids are coin-like stacks of membranes that contain molecules of chlorophyll and other pigments used in photosynthesis.
   (iii) grana are stacks of thylakoids.

b. **Chromoplasts** are angular-shaped plastids that develop from chloroplasts. They produce and store the yellow, orange, or red carotenoid pigments and give plants their colors.

c. **Leucoplasts** are colorless plastids that include amyloplasts which both synthesize and store various materials in the plant cell. Two types of leucoplasts occur in plants, **amyloplasts** and **elaioplasts**.
   (1) amyloplasts both store and synthesize starch.
   (2) elaioplasts synthesize and store plant oils.

7. **Lysosomes** are packets of digestive enzymes. Lysosomes temporarily bind with food vacuoles to digest their contents. The digested contents then pass through the lysosome membrane into the cytoplasm as nutrients. When the cell dies, lysosomes rupture and their enzymes are released to digest the cell contents in a process called autophagy or "self-eating". This removes the dead cell and recycles its nutrient content for living cells.

8. **Vacuoles** are membrane-bound storage organelles in cells that store food (food vacuoles) and packets of waste (excretory vacuoles). In some plant cells vacuoles comprise 80-90% of the cell interior. Vacuoles store mostly water and substances dissolved in water.

9. **Vesicles** are typically small, membrane-bound substances that have been taken into the plant cell via endocytosis or secreted. They are typically used for transport of substances manufactured by the plant cell or received by the plant cell.

F. Microtubules and Microfilaments

1. The **cytoskeleton** consists of a series of tubules in the cytoplasm that strengthens and gives shape to cells. It consists of protein microtubules and microfilaments that form a kind of scaffolding extending through the cytoplasm.

2. **Microtubules** are thin, unbranched and hollow fibers of protein. Most occur just within the cell membrane where they control addition of cellulose to the cell wall. Microtubules in the plant cell aid in the movement of flagella and cilia, still others are associated with formation of spindle fibers in cell division to be discussed below.

3. **Cilia** and **flagella** are types of filaments associated with the outer surface of the cell and function in cell movement.

G. Cyclosis is Cytoplasmic Streaming or Cytoplasmic Movement

1. In many cells the protoplasm is continuously moving in slow motion in a circular pattern of flow around and around. Fluid, minerals, gases, and organelles are carried around the cytoplasm by this movement which is called cyclosis or cell streaming.

2. Cyclosis probably helps distribute nutrients and organelle products throughout the cell interior. Bundles of microtubules many be responsible for causing cyclosis.

H. The Cell Nucleus

1. The nucleus is the headquarters and control center of the cell. The nucleus of plant cells is generally located within the cell. Its major components include the nuclear membrane, chromosomes, and one or more miniature nucleuses called nucleolus.

2. The nucleus is protected and surrounded by a nuclear membrane. The chemical structure and composition of the nuclear membrane is similar to the other membranes in the cell. The nuclear membrane may be continuous with the ER membrane.

3. The nucleus contains the chromosomes which are combinations of DNA and protein beads. These chromosomes contain the chemical blueprints of cells. In this sense, the chromosomes contain all the information needed to run the cell. They are also the units of heredity.

4. Within the nucleus are one or more organelles, each called a nucleolus. The nucleolus are rich in RNA and are the site of ribosomal RNA and messenger RNA synthesis.

III. The Cell Cycle
A. The Life Cycle of a cell is called the Cell Cycle.

1. Events in the life cycle of a cell include growth, maturity, one or more cycles of reproduction, and ultimately death.

2. Cell reproduction is also known as cell division or cell replication. During cell reproduction, the "mother cell" divides into two daughter cells.

3. Cell reproduction results in new cells for plant growth in higher plants. In single-celled plants like the protistans cell division results in the production of two new individuals.

4. Cell reproduction functions to (a) produce growth (b) replace dead and dying cells (c) to increase population size of protistans.

5. The process of cell reproduction is extremely regular and insures the qualitatively and quantitatively equal distribution of the hereditary factors among the cells.

6. Cell reproduction in plants occur in **meristematic** tissue located in root and stem tips and in **vascular cambium** located either interior or just under the surface. In herbaceous and most woody plants, cell reproduction also takes place in second meristem called **cork cambium** which is located between the cambium and the bark.

7. Cell reproduction by prokaryotic cells is primarily by binary fission. Where the parent cell divides into two daughter cells, each of which receives a single copy of the chromosome.

8. Two basic events are recognized in eukaryotic cell reproduction, **mitosis** and **cytokinesis**.

9. Mitosis concerns the replication or copying and assortment of chromosomes. Mitosis is sometimes termed **karyokinesis**.

10. **Cytokinesis** involves the replication of cell organelles, division of the cytoplasm into two daughter cells and subsequent growth of the daughter cells.

B. The Stages of Mitosis

1. Each mitotic division is a continuous process, with each stage imperceptibly transitioning into the next one. For clarity we divide mitosis into 5 stages, **interphase**, **prophase**, **metaphase**, **anaphase**, and **telophase**.

2. Interphase is called the resting stage, but actually the cell is active with the normal events of life. Often 90% of cell reproduction time occurs in this stage. Technically, interphase is considered the preparation period for cell division. During interphase, chromosomes make exact copies of themselves. Any error that occurs during this copying process is called a mutation. At the end of interphase the dividing cell has two complete sets of chromosomes, the original and a complete copy. Each of the chromosomes is called a **chromatid**. Each pair of chromatids is held together by thread-like proteins called a **centromere**. Interphase can be subdivided into three distinct periods:

   a. The G_1 **phase** is also called the First Gap Period. The G_1 period is characterized by cell growth in preparation for mitosis.

   b. The **S** phase is also called the Synthesis Period. During the S phase the chromosomes are duplicated as described above.

   c. During the G_2 phase the proteins and enzymes necessary for constructing the spindle bundles are manufactured.

3. During **prophase** the nuclear membrane dissolves. The centrioles migrate towards opposite ends of the cell and weave a spindle bundle that will extend to each of the chromatids. The spindle fibers (microtubules) radiate out from two invisible poles at the opposite ends of the dividing cell.

4. During **metaphase** the chromosomes are lined up in the center of the dividing cell and the centrioles arrive at opposite ends of the cell.

  a. In humans, for example 46 pairs of chromosomes are lined up in the center.

  b. The spindle fibers extending from the centrioles attach to the centromeres of each 92 chromatids.

5. In **anaphase** the centromere ruptures and the chromosomes migrate to opposite ends of the cell, actually towards the centrioles. They are pulled by the contraction action of the spindle fibers.

6. **Telophase** marks the culmination of mitosis, in which the chromatids arrive at opposite ends of the cell. A nuclear membrane reforms as the dividing cell splits into two separate daughter cells. Each of the daughter cells ends up with a complete set of chromosomes.

C. The Events of Cytokinesis

1. Cytokinesis is the second process of cell duplication.

2. During cytokinesis, the organelles are duplicated, or in the case of mitochondria, chloroplasts, and certain other organelles, duplicate themselves using their own DNA material.

3. Growth and further differentiation of each of the daughter cell also occurs during cytokinesis.

4. At the end of cytokinesis the dividing cell splits into two daughter cells. This process begins when microtubules collect at the middle of the dividing cell (called the equatorial plate) to form a **phragmoplast** or keg-shaped body which will become the new cell wall.

5. Directed by the action of Golgi bodies, the **cell plate** grows outward from the middle of the cell to join with the plasma membrane, thereby effectively splitting the dividing cell into the two new daughter cells. Cellulose is deposited within this new membrane to form the middle lamella shared by the two new daughter cells.

D. Summary of the Chromosomes during Cell Reproduction

1. Chromosomes are DNA molecules that extend through the nucleoplasm when the cell is not replicating. Unwound chromosomes called **chromatin**.

2. During mitosis the DNA chromatin coils around beads of proteins to form the familiar cell structures called **chromosomes**.

3. Each organism species has a specific number of chromosomes. Humans, for example, have 46, amoeba have 6, and a crayfish has 200.

4. At the end of mitosis each of the daughter cells has a complete set of chromosomes.

5. At the end of mitosis each of the cells is "new" in the sense that neither cells is "older" than the other. Thus, cells are in a sense immortal.

Multiple Choice Self-Test

_____ 1. The outer layer or boundary of a plant cell is the: (a) cell membrane (b) lipid
(c) lamella (d) cell wall (e) all of the above.

_____ 2. The outer layer or boundary of an animal cell is the: (a) cell wall (b) lipid layer
(c) middle lamella (d) cell membrane (e) outer lamella

_____ 3. The vacuoles of cells are used for the storage of: (a) water (b) salts (c) minerals
(d) sugars (e) all of the above (f) none of the above.

_____ 4. Which does not belong with the others? (a) mitochondria (b) nucleolus
(c) chloroplast (d) vacuole (e) endoplasmic recticulum

_____ 5. Eukaryotic cells differ from plant prokaryotic cells in having: (a) chromosomes
(b) genes (c) DNA (d) nucleus (e) a cell wall.

_____ 6. These cell structures form the skeleton of the cell: (a) cell membrane
(b) cytoskeleton (c) plastids (d) cell wall (e) all of the above

_____ 7. This organelle produces energy to run the cell: (a) ribosome (b) mRNA
(c) mitochondria (d) nucleolus (e) nucleus

_____ 8. Structures in the cell wall that strengthen and reinforce it: (a) lignin
(b) cellulose (c) pectin (d) all of the above (e) none of the above.

_____ 9. Exporting large substances through the cell wall is termed: (a) exocytosis
(b) osmosis (c) diffusion (d) active transport

Some Key Terms to Remember

Mitosis	interphase	prophase
Metaphase	telophase	cytokinesis
Anaphase	DNA	mRNA
tRNA	ribosome	mitochondria
cytoskeleton	prokaryotic	eukaryotic
cytoplasm	Robert Hooke	cell principle
cell wall	lamella	genes

Matching Self-Test

_____ 1. Chromosomes duplicate during this stage   a. interphase
_____ 2. Nuclear membranes disappear   b. prophase
_____ 3. Chromosomes line up in center of cell   c. metaphase
_____ 4. Chromosomes migrate to opposite ends   d. anaphase
_____ 5. Nuclear membrane reforms   e. telophase
_____ 6. Cell splits into two new cells, organelles duplicate   f. cytokinesis
_____ 7. Movement or streaming of cytoplasm is?   g. cyclosis

Visual Understanding Self-Test

1. In the circles provided draw the chromosome placement for an organism that has 4 chromosomes for metaphase, anaphase, and telophase stages of mitosis.

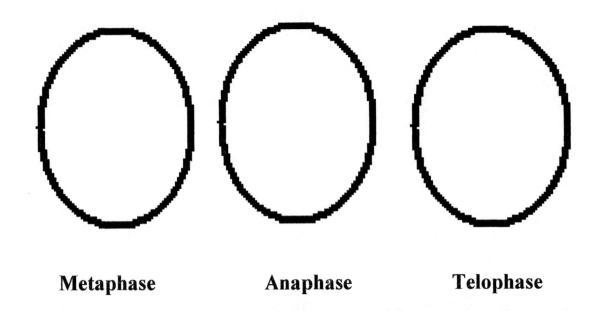

| **Metaphase** | **Anaphase** | **Telophase** |

Understanding Processes Self-Test

1. On a separate sheet of paper diagram and describe the events and relationships of protein synthesis. Be sure to include the following in the correct order: amino acids, mRNA, gene, protein, chromosome, DNA, tRNA.

2. Horsetail, otherwise called *Equisetum*, contains no fewer than 216 chromosomes in each of its cells. Supply the following information per mitotic cell or resulting cells:

        Number of chromosomes at the completion of interphase _____

        Number of homologous chromosomes prior to mitosis _____

        Number of chromosomes during metaphase   _____

        Number of chromosomes during cytokineses   _____

Visual Understanding Self-Test

1. Label the diagram of the cell illustrated below using: cell wall, vacuole, nucleus, nucleolus, mitochondria, chloroplast, endoplasmic recticulum, lamella, dictysome

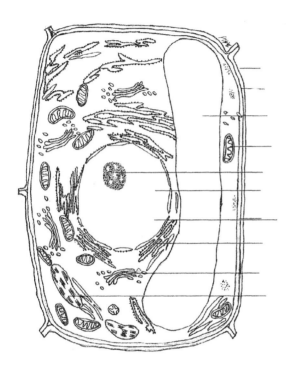

Visual Self-Test
Identify and label the different stages of mitosis seen in this representative diagram.

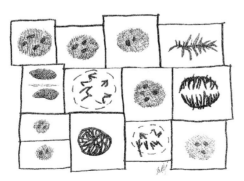

Chapter 4 Plant Tissues

This chapter will consider the following questions:
- ➢ What are plant tissues?
- ➢ What are the basic kinds of tissues in plants?
- ➢ What are the structures and functions of the major plant tissues?
- ➢ What are complex tissues and what are their basic functions in plants?

I. Plant Structure, Organs and Tissues
A. Defining the terms
1. All plants are comprised of millions and sometimes billions of cells that form the major plant structures such as the roots, stems, leaves and flowers.
2. Roots, stems, and leaves of a plant are called **organs**. Organs are comprised of several kinds of tissues which collectively perform one or more plant functions.
3. **Tissues** are groups of cells that have a similar morphology (shape and structure) and perform a particular function.

B. Kinds of Tissues
1. Plants have two basic types of tissues, **meristematic** tissues and **nonmeristematic** tissues.
   a. Primary tissues form the primary plant body.
   b. Secondary tissues form the woody, secondary growth of plants.

II. Meristematic Tissues
A. Definition of Meristematic Tissues
1. Meristematic tissues are comprised of cells that actively divide.
2. The basic kinds of meristematic tissues in plants include **apical meristems**, **lateral meristems (= vascular cambium)**, and **cork cambium**.

B. Apical Meristems are also known as Primary Tissues.
1. Apical meristem represent the growing tissue of the young plant. They are found at or near the tips of roots and shoots. They increase the length, or height of the plant and the depths of the roots by adding new cells by mitosis. They produce the primary meristems which in turn produce almost all of the primary tissue of the plant.

2. Cells of apical meristems are small and box-like with a large nucleus.
3. Apical meristems produce three kinds of primary tissues, **protoderm**, **ground meristem**, and **procambium**.
   a. **Protoderm** produces the epidermis that covers the roots, stems, and leaves as well as specialized cells such as root hairs.
   b. **Ground meristem** is interior to the apical meristem and produces the bulk of the stem or root. Three tissues produced by ground meristem include parenchyma, collenchyma, schlerenchyma.
   c. **Procambium** differentiates into the xylem and phloem transport system of the plant.

C. Lateral Meristems
1. Lateral Meristems are also known as **vascular cambium**
2. Lateral meristems begin as individual, self-perpetuating cells called **initials**.
3. Lateral meristems arise as a thin branching cylinder extending along the length of stems and roots of most perennials and many herbaceous annuals. The growth of lateral meristems increases the size or girth of plant.

D. Cork Cambium
1. Cork cambium is produced as secondary tissue along the stems and roots.
2. Cork cambium is located outside of the vascular cambium to form a tube-like structure.
3. Cork cambium produces the **periderm**, or secondary tissues that may replace or cover the epidermis of stems and roots. It produces bark in older plants.

E. Intercalary Meristems
1. Intercalary meristems are the reproducing tissues found in grasses.
2. Intercalary meristems occur in the nodes of grasses.
3. Their activity increases the length (or height) of grasses.

III. Non-Meristematic Tissues
A. Nonmeristematic tissues are produced by Meristematic Tissues.
1. Although produced by actively dividing meristematic tissues, nonmeristematic cells are no longer able to divide.
2. Nonmeristematic cells assume specialized shapes and functions.
3. Three kinds of nonmeristematic tissues are recognized, **parenchyma**, **collenchyma**, and **schlerenchyma**.

B. Parenchyma
1. Parenchyma is the most abundant type of nonmeristematic tissues in plants. It is especially widespread in advanced plants and makes up most of the

cortex of stems and roots, leaf mesophyl, the pith of stems, and comprises most of the body of fruits.

2. Most parenchyma cells are large and thin-walled with a primary cell wall.

3. Metabolically, parenchyma functions in photosynthesis, respiration, transport of water, food, and minerals, and in storage.

4. Parenchyma storage cells in stems and roots often have large vacuoles for the storage of starch, grains, oils, tannins, crystals, and other plant products and secretions.

5. Several kinds of parenchyma cells are recognized, based on their function.

    a. **Aerenchyma**-have connected air spaces useful for floatation in aquatic plants.

    b. **Chlorenchyma**-has many chloroplasts for photosynthesis and is common in leaves.

    c. **Parenchyma**-bulk of plant, edible parts of most fruits and vegetables.

    d. **Transfer cells**-some parenchyma develop irregular extensions on their surface to increase surface area for absorption.

C. Collenchyma

1. Collenchyma consists of long-lived cells with thick walls, alive at maturity.

2. Collenchyma occurs just beneath epidermis of plants, forming strands or layers along the stems, petioles, and around vascular tissues.

3. Collenchyma cells are longer than wide with strong and pliable cell walls.

4. A basic function is to provide strong but flexible support for growing leaves and flowers.

D. Sclerenchyma

1. Sclerenchyma consists of cells that have thick, tough walls impregnated with lignin for added strength. Sclerenchyma functions to support the young plant and provide the protective hardness of shells that surround seeds. Sclerenchyma cells are dead at maturity but continue to support the plant.

2. There are two types of schlerenchyma cells; **sclerids** and **fibers**.

    a. Sclerids are randomly distributed in plant tissues; two common examples of sclerids include the gritty stone cells in fruits such as pears and in the shells of nuts.

    b. Fibers-found associated with different tissues in roots, stems, leaves, and fruits. Fibers are long thin cells with a central cavity. Fibers are organized in long bundles or strands that provide both strength and flexibility to the plant. Commercially, fibers extracted from plants have been used for thousands of years in the manufacture of textiles. Examples include rope, hemp, cotton and linen.

IV. Complex Plant Tissues
A. Types and Functions of Complex Tissues
1. Complex tissues are plant tissues formed from two or more kinds of cells. Plants have several basic kinds of complex tissues.

B. Secretory Tissues
1. Secretory tissues consists of cells or tissues that manufacture and release chemicals. Familiar secretory products include nectar, oils, mucilage, latex and resins.
2. Some secretory tissues excrete waste products. Some produce hormones that function as chemical messengers to stimulate plant activity.
3. Examples of commercially important substances produced by secretory tissues include pine, resins, rubber, mint oil, and opium.

C. Epidermis
1. The epidermis is the outermost layer of cells of all young plants. It is produced by protoderm.
2. The epidermis is usually one cell thick but additional cell layers may be added in response to changing environmental conditions. In some plants such as orchids, figs, and peppers, the epidermis can be considerably thicker.
3. Most epidermal cells secrete a layer of fatty substance called cutin on their outer wall which, along with waxes, form the **cuticle**. The cuticle provides an additional layer of protection and water proofing for the plant. The cuticle of some plants is harvested for commercial uses; an example is the carnauba wax extracted from leaves of wax palm.
4. Epidermal cells produce:
    a. Root hairs--- these are tubular extensions of roots used for absorption.
    b. Guard cells---surround stomata in leaves.
    c. Glands---secrete various substances.
    d. Hairs---consist of from one to several cells and are used for anchoring.

D. Xylem
1. The xylem is the plant's major tissue for the conduction of water and minerals.
2. The major cells of xylem are **vessels** and **tracheids**. Parenchyma cells, fibers, vessels, and ray cells are also found in xylem.
    a. **Vessels** are long tubes made up of individual cells joined end to end to form hollow conducting tubes through which water and minerals move.
    b. **Tracheid** cells are common in conifers and ferns. They have tapered ends that overlap to create end to end tubes. Small pits in these end walls provide passageways for movement of water and minerals.
3. Ray cells are long-lived parenchyma cells that form horizontal rows by special ray initials of the vascular cambium. In woody plants ray cells radiate out from center like the spokes of a wheel.

E. Phloem.

1. The phloem is the plant's major tissue for the conduction of food.
2. Phloem is a primary or secondary tissue derived from cambium cells that also produce xylem.
3. Phloem is comprised of **sieve-tube elements** and **companion cells** along with smaller amounts of parenchyma cells, ray cells, and fibers.
    a. Sieve-tube cells are cells laid end to end forming long tubes. Their end walls have many plasmodesmata for entry and exit of transported food.
    b. Companion cells provide support for sieve tube cells.
4. Ferns and cone bearing trees (the evergreens) have **sieve cells** like sieve tube cells which overlap at their ends rather than meet end to end.
5. Transport of food through living phloem cells consumes energy.

F. Periderm

1. This secondary tissue replaces the epidermis of stems and roots in older plants.
2. Periderm is the outer bark of woody vegetation and is dead at maturity.
3. Periderm is comprised of cork cambium, cork, and phelloderm.
    a. Cork cambium is a layer of meristematic tissue that produces cork tissue on the outside and phelloderm on the inside of the layer.
    b. Cork is composed of box-like cells which are impregnated with the lipid **suberin** which forms a protective covering and also helps make the bark waterproof.
    c. Phelloderm is living parenchyma tissue that has the ability to repair or replace injured, diseased, or damaged cork cambium.
4. Some cork cambium (e.g., cherries, birches) contains small pockets of parenchyma cells that protrude to surface of periderm as **lenticels** which function in gas exchange.

Key Terms to Remember

Complex tissues	meristems	periderm
Simple tissues	sclerencyma	sclerid
Lenticels	secretory tissue	vessels
Parenchyma	surberin	companion cells
Sieve cells	Sieve tube elements	ray cells
Xylem	phloem	tracheids

Multiple Choice Self-Test

_____ 1. Lenticels are: (a) groups of fiber cells (b) collenchyma (c) bunches of cork cells (d) parenchyma cell collections (e) sclerenchyma cells.

_____ 2. This lipid impregnates cork cells to make them waterproof: (a) protein (b) suberin (c) initials (d) wax (e) fiber (f) sclerid.

_____ 3. Which is a complex tissue: (a) epidermis (b) xylem (c) secretory tissue (d) phloem (e) all of the above (f) none of the above.

_____ 4. Self-perpetuating cells that become lateral meristems are: (a) rays (b) initials (c) collenchyma (d) periderm (f) all of the above.

_____ 5. Type of parenchyma cells that occur in aquatic plants: (a) collenchyma (b) initials (c) rays (d) aerenchyma (e) all of the above.

_____ 6. Cambium that differentiates into xylem and phloem: (a) lateral meristems (b) cork cambium (c) procambium (d) all of the above.

_____ 7. This lipid covers the outer wall of some epidermal cells: (a) suberin (b) cuticle (c) rays (d) bark (e) periderm.

_____ 8. These plant structures function in gas exchange: (a) rays (b) companion cells (c) lenticels (d) cork (e) epidermis (f) all of the above.

_____ 9. Sieve tube cells are connected by: (a) pits (b) sieve plates (c) cell wall (d) companion cells (e) tracheids (f) all of the above.

_____ 10. Peach stones or peach pits have a hard outer covering of: (a) fibers (b) sclerids (c) guard cells (d) collenchyma cells (e) tracheids.

Matching Self-Test

_____ 1. Food storage tissue   a. sieve-tube cells
_____ 2. Mitotically dividing cells   b. lenticels
_____ 3. Food storage cells   c. vessels
_____ 4. Pockets of parenchyma cells that extend to surface   d. parenchyma
_____ 5. Long hollow tubes for water movement   e. meristem
_____ 6. Phloem cells that transport food   f. periderm
_____ 7. Secondary tissue that replaces epidermis of stems

Matching Self-Test

_____ 1. Orchid velamen roots produced by   a. secretory cells
_____ 2. Specialized epidermal cells of roots   b. velamen roots
_____ 3. Nectar, oils, latex, resins produced by   c. root hairs
_____ 4. Aromatic substances produced by   d. dermal tissues
_____ 5 Plants live a single year then die   e. biannuals
_____ 6. Plants live two years and then die   f. perennials
_____ 7. Plants live for many years   g. annuals

Identify the primary regions of meristematic growth through the longitudinal section of a stem. Some areas to identify include elongation zone, primary phloem, cambium meristem, primary xylem, pith, and apical meristem.

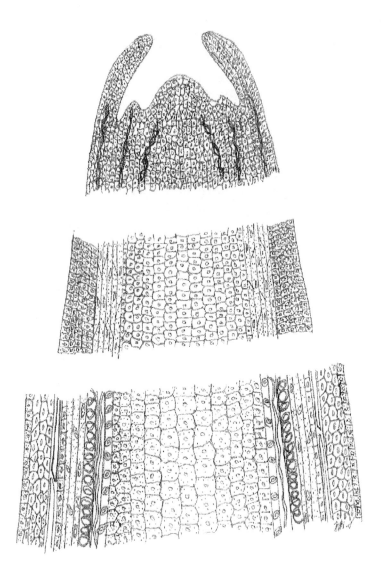

Chapter 5 Plant Stems

This chapter considers the following questions

- ➢ What are plant stems?
- ➢ What is the external structure of stems?
- ➢ How do stems grow and develop?
- ➢ What are types of stems found in plants?
- ➢ What are examples of modified and specialized stems?

I. What are Stems?
A. General Introduction

1. Plant stems comprise the above ground portion of the visible plant. Some plants have specialized, underground stems (e.g., bulbs, corms) that will be discussed later.
2. Plant stems are very useful in everyday life. Anything built of wood comes from stem.
3. Stems produced by meristems are called shoot systems and are usually erect.
4. In many plants, stems can be subdivides into a trunk, branches, and twigs.
5. Stems functions include (1) providing support for leaves (2) providing storage for sugars and starches produced by photosynthesis (3) providing storage for water and minerals (4) conducting water, food, and minerals via xylem and phloem.

B. External Structure of Stems

1. The stem forms an axis for the support of the upper part of the plant and attachment of leaves.
2. Leaves may attach along the stem either opposite one another (opposite), alternately along the stem (alternate) or in a spiral around the stem (whorled).
3. Area where leaves attached is called a **node**.
4. Stem region between nodes is called an **internode**.
5. Leaves are attached to the stem by a **petiole**.
6. **Buds** occur at the angle between petiole and stem.
   - a. The angle is called **axil** and the bud in an axil is called an **axillary bud**.
   - b. Buds may become branches, leaves or flowers.
   - c. Buds are protected by **bud scales** which fall off as growth continues.
   - d. The **terminal bud** is at the end of the twig. Growth at terminal bud extends length of twig.

7. **Bud scales** of terminal bud leave scars around twig after they fall off in spring.
   - a. We can age a twig by counting bud scale scars along it.
   - b. The distance between bud scale scars represents the growth of the twig during that particular growing season. The distance between the last bud scale scars and the tip of the twig represents last season's growth.
8. Some leaves have paired appendages called **stipules** at their base. As stipules fall off **stipule scars** are left on the twig.
9. **Leaf scars** along a twig mark the site of a leaf before it fell off the plant.
   - a. Deciduous plants have leaf scars with dormant axillary buds above them in fall.
   - b. The **bundle scars** within leaf scars mark the location of vascular conduction tissues(the xylem and phloem). Botanists use the configuration of leaf scars and the number of bundle scars to key woody plants.

C. Origin of development of stems

1. Stems originate and develop from apical meristems at the end of each stem. The apical meristem is dormant until spring.
2. Apical meristem represents the terminal bud which is surrounded by leaf primordia which in turn is surrounded and protected by bud scales.
3. Cells in apical meristem undergo mitosis and develop into 3 primary meristems which produce the primary tissues of stems.
4. The meristems produce protoderm, procambium, and ground meristem which in turn differentiates to give rise to specific portions of the stem.
   - a. Protoderm is the outermost meristem and gives rise to epidermis and the cuticle of the stem.
   - b. Procambium is internal to protoderm and produces the primary xylem cells and primary phloem of the stem.
   - c. Ground meristem is comprised mostly of parenchyma cells that give rise to much of the stem's interior or central core.
     - (1) Pith is the center of the stem comprised of large cells. At maturity the pith cells die leaving a hollow space in the interior of the stem.
     - (2) Cortex is more extensive than pith but may eventually be replaced. In woody plants both pith and cortex may be destroyed.
5. Leaf primordia along the stem become mature leaves and buds. As they develop, they produce a strand of xylem and phloem called a leaf trace.
6. A **leaf trace** along a stem results when xylem and phloem branch originate from main vascular cylinder and leave a gap.

7. **Vascular cambium** refers to the lateral meristem cells that occur between the xylem and phloem. In woody plants the vascular cambium produces secondary tissues which increases the girth (width) of the stem.
   a. Secondary tissue produced on the inside of the vascular cambium includes xylem components---tracheids, vessel elements, fibers that make **secondary xylem**.
   b. Secondary tissue produced on the outside is **secondary phloem**.
8. Growth of the **cork cambium** or **phellogen** lateral meristem in woody plants also increases diameter of the stem.
   a. The cork cells produced by the cork cambium contain suberin for protection and water proofing the stem.
   b. Cells produced by phellogen become the hard and protective bark of woody stems.

D. Tissue Patterns of Stems
1. Tissue patterns in stems differ between monocots and dicots and differ between annual plants (annuals) and plants that may live several years (perennials).
2. Stems can also be classed as woody or herbaceous.
   a. Woody stems of trees and shrubs contain secondary growth of xylem.
   b. Herbaceous stems of annuals (grasses, many flowers) consist of soft, primary tissue and lacks secondary growth.
3. The central vascular bundles of primary xylem, primary phloem and pith are called **steles**.
   a. **Protostele** is the simplest form, consisting of a solid core of xylem surrounded by phloem. Protosteles occur in primitive seed plants, whisk ferns, club mosses.
   b. **Siphonostele** are found in ferns and consists of a tubular-stele with pith in center.
   c. **Eustele** consists of primary xylem and primary phloem arranged in vascular bundles as seen in modern flowering plants.
4. **Herbaceous dicot stems** are annuals that complete their life cycle in one season.
   a. Herbaceous dicot stems consist of soft, primary tissues and lack woody growth.
   b. The xylem and phloem are located in **vascular bundles** that occur in a ring-like pattern between the pith and the epidermis. Cambium may be located in the vascular bundle or may form a ring around the stem.
5. **Woody dicots** live several years and have secondary woody growth.
   a. First year's growth consists of primary tissues which are mostly replaced with woody secondary growth in subsequent years.
   b. The vascular cambium layer of woody dicots produces secondary xylem and phloem.

(1) secondary xylem is the wood that comprises the bulk of the stem interior.

(2) secondary phloem occurs as a series of thinner layers on the outside of the vascular cambium.

c. Eventually, woody growth displaces the initial first year or primary growth in the stem.

6. As the tree or shrub ages the stem becomes organized into distinct regions of heartwood and sapwood.

7. In larger woody stems the vascular cambium produces horizontal xylem rays for transporting water and fluids laterally through the thickened stem. Xylem rays are comprised mostly of modified parenchyma tissue.

a. The newly formed xylem is called **sapwood**.

b. **Heartwood** is formed when parenchyma cells around vascular bundles grow into pits in the walls of xylem and phloem to eventually fill the cell cavities with resins and gums that form the darker heartwood. Such accumulations are called **tyloses** and prevent conduction of water and food.

c. The heartwood may eventually rot away without affecting tree.

8. **Annual rings**. Early secondary xylem produced in spring consists mostly of large xylem vessel elements and is termed **spring wood**. As season progresses the xylem becomes smaller and consists mostly of tracheids. It is called **summer wood**. The change between spring and summer wood results in **annular rings**.

a. Vascular cambium produces more xylem than phloem and xylem cells have stronger and more rigid cells than phloem. Thus bulk of tree trunk is annual rings of wood.

b. Rings tell age of the tree and also give information as to climatic conditions.

c. Ring cores are taken by a tool called **increment borer**.

9. **Rays** are clearly seen in transverse sections of tree trunks. Rays radiate out from center across annual rings. Ray in xylem is **xylem ray**, in phloem is **phloem ray**. Rays are parenchyma cells that live10 years or more and conduct nutrients and water laterally.

10. **Softwoods** are another name for evergreens or cone bearing trees such as pines, spruces, and firs. The xylem of these trees consists only of tracheids, hence lack fibers and vessel elements. Without fibers the wood of these trees is softer than hardwoods. **Resin canals** scattered in the xylem of softwoods are tube like and lined with cells that secrete resin into the xylem cavity. Examples of resin secretions include Frankincense and myrrh.

11. The xylem of deciduous trees such as birches, oaks, and maples consists of fibers along with vessel elements and is called **hardwoods**.

12. **Bark** is the outer covering of the woody stem. It consists of phloem, cork, cork cambium, phellogen, and phelloderm. It protects the tree from mechanical injury, insects and diseases, provides water proofing, and conducts food.
    a. **Inner bark** consists of primary and secondary phloem.
    b. **Outer bark** consists of cork tissue and cork cambium.
    c. Cells of phloem and cortex eventually are crushed by new cells from the cork cambium which produces alternating layers of crushed phloem and cork.
    d. The phloem layers nearest the cambium conduct sugars from the roots to the leaves for use in respiration.

13. **Laticifers** are specialized cells or ducts that occur in 20 families of herbaceous and woody flowering plants. Common in phloem but elsewhere as well. Resemble vessels and form extensive branched network to produce **latex**, which is a thick fluid, white to red orange, consisting of gums, protein, sugars, oils, salts, alkaloidal drugs, enzymes. Their function is unknown but they may help to close wounds and resist disease organisms. Latex producing species include rubber, opium, poppy.

14. **Monocotyledonous Stems** are typified by plants such as grasses and lilies.
    a. Monocot stems lack vascular cambium and cork cambium so consequently have no secondary vascular tissues or cork.
    b. The stem is covered with epidermis.
    c. Xylem and phloem occurs in discrete vascular bundles that are scattered throughout the stem, instead of being in rings.
    d. Each bundle has the xylem closest to center of stem and phloem closest to the surface.
    e. The xylem contains two large vessels with several small vessels between. The first formed xylem cells stretch and collapse under stresses of further growth leaving irregularly shaped air space toward base of the bundle.
    f. The phloem consists only of sieve tubes and companion cells.
    g. Each vascular bundle is surrounded by sclerenchyma cells.
    h. Wheat, barley, rice, oats, and rye lack vascular cambium but have an intercalary meristem at the base of the node—their plant stem grows in length much more than in girth.

15. Growth in stems of largest monocots such as palms is produced by parenchyma cells that continue to divide and enlarge for support. Houseplant monocots such as *Ti* plants and *Dracaena* have a secondary meristem which develops as a cylinder that extends throughout the length of the stem.

16. Monocot fibers obtained from broom corn, Manilla hemp, sisal are actually vascular bundles scrapped free of surrounding parenchyma cells by

hand. These are not as strong or durable as dicot fibers as they are not really fibers.

II. Specialized Stems
A. Stems vary considerably in plants.
1. Many show interesting specializations.
2. Many stems are commercially valuable for food and other plant products.
3. Not all stems are erect shoot systems but all have nodes, internodes and axillary buds.

B. Rhizomes
1. Rhizomes resemble roots but are actually horizontal stems that grow beneath the soil surface. Or near the soil surface. They permit vegetative propagation of certain plants.
2. Rhizomes superficially resemble roots, but have scale-like leaves and axillary buds.
3. Rhizomes may produce adventitious roots along rhizome as in mangroves.
4. Rhizomes of grasses, ferns, and iris contain parenchyma tissues for starch storage.

C. Stolons
1. Stolons are also called runners that extend horizontally just above the ground surface.
2. Stolons typically have long internodes and may develop buds at their ends.
3. Examples of plants with stolons include saxifrages, strawberries, and spider plants.

D. Tubers, Bulbs, and Corms
1. Tubers, bulbs, and corms are swollen stems that typically function as food storage organs.
   a. Tubes have swollen internodes and are rich in food. They usually form at the tip of a stolon, after which the stolon dies, isolating the tuber. Potatoes are tubers; the eyes of the potato are the stem nodes while the axillary bud is the axil of a scale-like leaf. The small ridges in mature tubers are actually the leaf scars.
   b. Bulbs are large buds with a small stem at their lower end. Bulbs are surrounded by numerous fleshy leaves that store food. Examples include, onions, lilies, hyacinths and tulips.
   c. Corms are like bulbs but are almost completely covered papery, scale-like leaves. Food is stored in the stem as in crocuses and gladioli.

E. Examples of Other Specialized Stems
    1. Cacti stem is fat and fleshy for storage of water.
    2. Some spines are actually modified stems. Honey locust spines are protective. Thorns of Roses and raspberries are derived from epidermis rather than from true stems.
    3. Some tendrils of climbing plants such as grape and Boston ivy are modified stems.

III. Economics of Wood
A. Commercial Uses of Wood
    1. Wood is used to build houses and furniture.
    2. Since nearly half of freshly cut wood is comprised of water, it must be dried to reduce the water content to less than 10%. This process is called seasoning. Otherwise, the wood may warp and split along its rays.
    3. Dry wood is about 60-75% cellulose and 15-25 % lignin. Small amounts of gums, resins, oils, dyes, tannins, and starch make up the rest. Amounts of these substances determines use of wood.

B. Characteristics of Wood
    1. Density is the weight per unit volume of wood. Density is a function of the number of air cells in wood. Because of air in cells, wood has a specific gravity of less than 1, therefore wood floats in water. Balsa is the lightest wood. South American Ironwood is heaviest wood.
    2. Durability refers to the ability of wood to withstand decay organisms and insects. Less moisture in wood, the more durable it is. Tannins and oils also increase the durability of wood. If tannins content exceeds 15% wood may survive on forest floor for many years. Most durable American wood is cedar, catalpa, black locust, red mulberry, Osage orange. Least durable is cottonwood, willow, fur, and basswood.

C. Cutting Wood for Commercial Marketing
    1. Wood is cut in certain ways for the commercial market.
    2. Most logs are sawed longitudinally in one of two ways.
        a. Quartersawed wood is sawed along the radius and shows annual rings in side view which appear as conspicuous longitudinal streaks.
        b. Tangentially sawed wood is cut perpendicular to the rays and the annual rings appear as irregular bands of light and dark alternating streaks of patches.
        c. Knots in wood are actually the bases of lost branches that have been covered over by new annual rings.

D. Wood Products

1. Lumber- at least half of the wood commercially cut in the United States is used for lumber. Most of this wood is used for housing construction and the manufacture of furniture.

2. Sawdust and waste resulting from cutting is used in the preparation of pulp and particle board. Waste chips are also converted into particle board, pulp, or used for the paper or cardboard industry.

3. Veneer-is thin sheet of wood glued over cheaper wood to make beautiful. Examples of Veneer include attractive and expensive hardwoods such as cherry, walnut, tiger maple. Extremely thin sheets of this valuable wood is cut and glued to make the veneer.

4. Pulp is a wood product often used to make paper, synthetic fibers, plastics, linoleum. Pulp is also used as a filler for ice cream and bread.

5. Alcohols, acids, other uses---Hardwoods may be treated to yield wood alcohol, acetic acid, charcoal, excelsior, cooperage (kegs, casks and barrels), railroad ties, boxes, crates, musical instruments, bowling pins, tool handles, pilings, cellophane, photographic film, and Christmas trees.

6. Fire Wood- In developing countries most of the wood used is for fire or cut for export as a cash crop. About 10% of the wood harvested in the United States is used for firewood but about 70% of the wood harvested in Brazil is burned for fuel. Burning of this wood contributes to greenhouse effect.

Multiple Choice Self Test

_____ 1. The tendrils of grapes and runners of strawberries are actually: (a) leaves (b) modified stems (c) rhizomes (d) roots (e) spreading roots.

_____ 2. A celery stick is actually: (a) stems (b) branches (c) leaves (d) petioles (e) tendrils (f) all of the above (g) none of the above.

_____ 3. Eating a potato is eating which part of a plant? (a) stem (b) root (c) leaf (d) root hairs (e) all of the above.

_____ 4. The meristem that gives rise to epidermis is: (a) cork cambium (b) procambium (c) ground meristem (d) vascular cambium (e) protoderm.

_____ 5. Which tissue is produced by ground meristem: (a) secondary xylem (b) primary xylem (c) phelloderm (d) cortex (e) primary phloem.

_____ 6. These paired structures occur at the base of the leaf: (a) leaf gaps (b) stipules (c) bundles (d) axillary buds (e) terminal buds (f) all of the above.

_____ 7. Which is applicable primarily to monocot stems? (a) cork cambium (b) pith and cortex (c) vascular bundles scattered across stem (d) vascular cambium (e) a ring of vascular bundles (f) none of the above.

_____ 8. The oldest part of a hundred year old tree: (a) tip of the roots (b) tip of the stem (c) in the leaves (d) center of the tree near the soil.

_____ 9. Annual rings of xylem illustrate: (a) secondary growth (b) primary growth (c) both primary and secondary growth (d) the oldest growth.

Label the following parts of a twig:

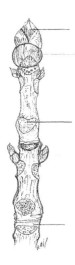

Label the basic components of a typical vascular plant.

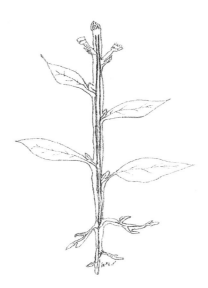

Visual Self-Test

Label the following components of a monocot and dicot stem: epidermis, phloem, vascular bundle, xylem, pith, cortex, primary phloem, secondary phloem, cambium.

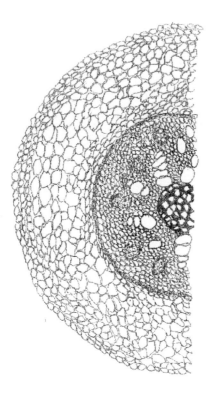
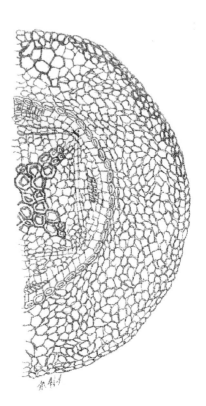

Chapter 6 Plant Roots

This chapter considers the following questions:
- ➤ What are roots?
- ➤ What are the functions of roots?
- ➤ What are the structures of roots?
- ➤ What are some examples of specialized roots?
- ➤ What are some of the human uses of roots?

I. Functions of Roots

A. Functions of Roots

1. Roots are the main structure for anchoring plants in the soil. They form a branching network that may constitute up to 1/3 dry weight of plant. Roots are usually 3-5 meters (about 10-16 feet) in depth but roots of mesquite roots grow more than 50 meters deep.
2. Roots are the plant's main organ for absorption of water and minerals in solution. Bulk of Feeder roots in the first upper meter of soil.
3. Roots store food for the plant.
4. Roots can also be a form of reproduction. For example, if trees are cut the stem sprouts frequently arise from the meristematic tissues of their roots.

B. Types of Roots

1. Root arises from radicle area of embryonic plant.
   a. Taproot is typically a large, single, central root from which adventitious roots are formed.
   b. Fibrous root system consists of numerous small adventitious roots. The fibrous root system of a single rye plant may have 15 million roots.
2. Root hairs on roots provide enormous amounts of additional surface area that greatly enhances absorption of water and minerals from the soil.
3. Most dicots have taproot systems while monocots usually have fibrous roots

C. Regions of Roots

1. A root has four distinct regions or zones. The root cap, zone of cell division, zone of elongation, and the zone of maturation. These extend from the root cap, which is the deepest into the soil, back towards the stem.
2. **Root Cap** is a thimble-shaped mass of parenchyma cells covering the root tip. The root cap protects the root from mechanical damage and abrasion as the root pushes into the soil.
   a. Golgi bodies of cells within the root cap secrete a slimy substance which lubricates the surface of the root cap, reducing friction as the root grows and forces its way deeper into the soil.

b. Root cap cells also respond to gravity. Cap cells have special plastids called **amyploplasts** (plastids with starch grains); the starch grains respond to the pull of gravity by collecting on the downward side of the root cap.

3. **Zone of Cell Division**- this area is located in the center of the root tip and is surrounded by the root cap. It contains special apical meristem as in stem tip. Cells within the zone of cell division typically divide every 12-36 hours. They are cuboidal cells with a large nucleus and few or no vacuoles. The root apical meristem consists of three areas:

   a. **Protoderm** forms the outer layer of cells or epidermis of the root.
   b. **Ground meristem** is located inside of the protoderm and forms the parenchyma cells of the root cortex.
   c. **Procambium** is a solid cylinder of tissue located within the center of the root and produces primary xylem and phloem.

4. **Region of Elongation** is a 1 centimeter long section of tissue located immediately behind the meristem. Cells in this region elongate many times their length. They grow by absorbing large volumes of water into large vacuoles that may eventually comprise to 90% of the cell volume. The elongation of these cells pushes the root deeper into the soil.

5. **Region of Maturation** is located immediately behind the zone of elongation. The now elongated cells in this region mature and differentiate into tissues. This region is also called the region of differentiation or root hair zone.

   a. **Root Hairs** develop directly from the root epidermis and extend into adjacent soil, adhering to soil particles.
      (1) Root hairs area actually not separate cells but instead are extensions of epidermal cells. Root hair area is just above the root cap.
      (2) Root hairs are extremely numerous, often numbering in the hundreds of thousands per cubic centimeter of soil.
      (3) Most root hairs are less than a centimeter in length.
      (4) Root hairs greatly increase area for absorption of water and minerals.

D. Structure and Function of Root Tissues

1. Structurally the root consists of an interior vascular cylinder or stele surrounded by a cortex which is covered by a layer of epidermis.
2. The epidermis is a thin layer of cells that gives rise to root hairs.
3. Interior to the epidermis is the cortex which consists of parenchyma cells used for food storage. The inner layer of the cortex is the endodermis which surrounds the vascular cylinder or stele.

   a. The endodermis is a single layer of cells with thickened walls that surrounds the interior vascular cylinder that comprises the center of the root. Each cell of the endodermis has a fatty covering of suberin termed a Casparian Strip that directs and regulates movement of water into the xylem.

4. Interior to the endodermis is cylinder of parenchyma cells called the stele which consists of four regions, the pericycle, xylem, and phloem.

    a. The pericycle is one or two layers of cells that lie just interior to the endodermis. The pericycle consists of meristem tissue that produces branch roots.

    b. Primary xylem forms a solid, star-shaped core in center of most dicot and conifer roots. Branch roots form opposite the xylem arms. In some dicots and many monocots the primary xylem forms a simple cylinder of conducting cells.

    c. Primary phloem forms in discrete patches between the arms of primary xylem.

    d. Vascular cambium in some woody and herbaceous dicots and conifers part of the pericylce between xylem arms forms a vascular cambium that produces secondary phloem to outside and secondary xylem to inside, eventually forming concentric cylinders with the primary tissue crushed out of existence.

5. Cork cambium- In woody plants, cork cambium arises in pericycle and give rise to an outer cork tissue or periderm as in stems. Old roots may have heartwood, sapwood, and annual rings. Monocot roots typically lack secondary meristems and also lack secondary growth in roots.

II. Specialized Roots
A. Food Storage Roots

1. Most roots store food but some roots are enlarged to store starch. Sweet potatoes, yams, dandelions, other plants, have extra cambial cells develop in parts of xylem of branch roots to produce extra parenchyma cells for additional storage or sugars.

2. Carrots, turnips, and similar plants store food via a combination of the stem and root.

B. Water Storage Roots

1. Members of the pumpkin family along with many plants of arid and semiarid habitats have large vacuoles in the cortex cells of their roots for water storage. A few of the many examples include manroot and calabazilla. These plants can subsist on water stored in the roots during dry periods.

C. Propagative Roots

1. Some plants have adventitious buds along roots that grow at or near the surface of the ground. The buds may develop into aerial stems called suckers

which have additional rootlet at base. Examples include cherries, pears and willows.

D. Pneumatophores
1. Roots or many swamp plants such as mangroves, develop spongy, air filled root segments that float on surface, absorbing gases directly from the air.

E. Contractile Roots
1. Some herbaceous dicots and monocots have roots that pull the plant deeper into the ground each year. Contractions occur when parenchyma cells thicken and constrict causing xylem elements to spiral like corkscrew.
2. Bulbs continue to be pulled down until stable area of temperature is reached. Dandelions.

F. Parasitic Roots
1. Some plants have no chlorophyll and must parasitize other plants. Parasitic plants typically have root-like projections called haustoria which develop where stem contacts host plant.
2. Haustoria invade outer tissues to extract plant fluids of host. Examples include fungi.

G. Mycorrhiza
1. Many conifers and some other flowering plants have mycorrhiza fungi associated with their roots in a mutualistic relationship. Fungus forms millions of thread like strands around and into the root that penetrate to the root cortex.
2. Both mycorrhiza fungi and root benefit and are dependent on each other. Root provides fungus with organic molecules while the mycorrhiza greatly enhances absorption of water and nutrients.
3. These fungus roots are necessary for survival of flowering plant, helping plants that live in areas where certain nutrients are scarce. Acid rain harms mycorrhiza and has been implicated in destruction of some conifer woodlands.

H. Root Nodules
1. Root nodules are conspicuous swellings on roots of legumes (e.g. peas and beans) which contain nitrogen fixing bacteria.
2. Nitrogen fixing bacteria extract nitrogen from the air to supplement the plant's nitrogen.

III. Economic Importance of Roots
A. Plants as Food Sources
1. Plants are an important source of food for humans. Many cultivated roots are biannual plants that store food in swollen taproot during the first year of growth and utilize it during second.
2. Some of the many examples of plant foods from roots include sugar beets, beets, turnips, rutabagas, parsnips, radishes, carrots, sweet potatoes, yams and cassava (tapioca).

B. Roots as Spice Sources
1. Sassafras, sarsaparilla, licorice, anglica and many other spices are obtained as extracts from roots.

C. Other Commercial Uses
1. Juices of sweet potatoes are used to make an alcoholic drink in Japan.
2. Red and brownish dyes are extracted from roots of members of the coffee family.
3. Extracts of roots for medical purposes (drugs) include aconite, ipecac, ginseng, gentian, and reserpine a tranquilizer.
4. An insecticide called rotenone is a root extract.

Multiple Choice Self Test

_____ 1. The pericycle of a root: (a) root hairs emerge from it (b) regulates water flow from the soil into the plant (c) organizes rootlets (d) all of the above.

_____ 2. Water must pass through these cell membranes to be absorbed by the plant: (a) xylem (b) epidermis (c) stomata (e) guard cells (f) all of the above.

_____ 3. Layer of wax that directs movement of water into the vascular cylinder of the root: (a) Casparian strip (b) endodermis (c) pericycle (d) stomata.

_____ 4. Root hairs originate from: (a) root cap (b) region of elongation (c) region of maturation (d) all of the above.

_____ 5. Which of the following is a root crop: (a) beets (b) cassava (c) sweet potato (d) carrot (e) all of the above (f) none of the above.

_____ 6. Food is stored in this root tissue: (a) cortex (b) epidermis (c) endodermis (d) phloem (e) pericycle (f) all of the above.

_____ 7. Thin walled cells of the endodermis are termed: (a) pericycle (b) transfer cells (c) passage cells (d) Casparian cells (e) all of the above.

_____ 8. Plant root nodules of legumes house colonies of: (a) bacteria (b) fungi (c) lichens (d) viruses (e) all of the above.

_____ 9. Special roots of swamp plants that grow on the surface of the water and absorb gases: (a) buttress roots (b) mycorrhizae (c) aerial roots (d) parasitic roots (e) pneumatophores.

Matching Self-Test

_____ 1. Branch roots arise from
_____ 2. Root hairs arise from
_____ 3. Root growth occurs from
_____ 4. Outer layer of a root
_____ 5. Innermost layer of a root

a. pericycle
b. meristem
c. epidermis
d. vascular cylinder
e. cortex

Visual Self-Test

Identify the following components of monocot and dicot roots: epidermis, cortex, endodermis, pericycle, xylem, parenchyma, primary xylem, secondary xylem, cambium, secondary phloem and primary phloem

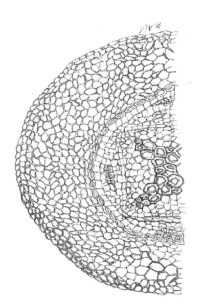
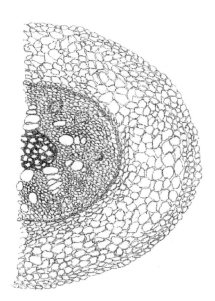

Chapter 7 **Plant Leaves**

This chapter considers the following questions:
- ➤ What are the functions of leaves?
- ➤ What is the external structure of leaves?
- ➤ What is the internal structure of leaves?
- ➤ What are some examples of specialized leaves?
- ➤ What causes the color changes and falling of leaves in autumn?

I. Functions of Leaves
A. Introducing Leaves
1. Leaves of plants occur in a wide variety of sizes, shapes, and colors.
2. Leaves are solar panels of plants that have two functions. Via photosynthesis they (1) convert a portion of sunlight (solar energy) into biomass and (2) convert a portion of solar energy into plant heat (called sensible heat production) that provides heat for metabolic activity in all living plants.
3. In many plants metabolic wastes are deposited in leaves. Thus, they are readily discarded when the plant sheds its leaves, which happens at least once a year in most plants. For example, excess salt (a type of toxic waste) is excreted in leaves of the desert plant called saltbush and conveniently lost when leaves are shed.
4. Evaporation of water from the stomata drives the movement of water through the xylem. Within the xylem, a drop of water is transported or "pulled" from the roots through the stems and into the leaves.

II. Leaf Arrangements and Types
A. Leaf Origins
1. Leaves develop from leaf primordial in buds. At maturity they consist of stalk called a petiole. A large flattened blade or lamina, and a network of veins which are the vascular bundles.
B. Leaf Arrangement
1. The actual arrangement of leaves on plant is called phyllotaxy.
2. Leaves may be opposite one another, alternate to one another or occur in whorls of three or more (whorled) around the stem.
3. Leaf shapes vary from one plant to another and can even vary on one plant.
   a. Simple leaves consist of an undivided blade.
   b. In compound leaves the leaf blade is divided into leaflets.
   c. A pinnately leaf consists of pairs of leaflets.

          d. Palmately compound--- all leaflets attached at same point at the end of petiole.

          e. Bipinnately compound---leaflets attached opposite one another on a long petiole.

4. The venation of a leaf refers to the way in which the veins are arranged along the length of the leaf.

          a. Pinnately veined leaves have a single main vein (the midrib) with secondary veins branching from it.

          b. In palmately veined leaves all veins are equal in size and emerge from petiole. Veins may be parallel to one another as in monocots or branching as in dicots.

          c. Dichotomous venation lacks a midrib or large veins-instead, veins fork evenly and progressively from base of blade to opposite margin. Gingko provides a good example.

III. The Structure of Leaves
A. Epidermis

1. The leaf epidermis consists of a single layer of cells covering the entire outer upper and lower surface.

2. On the lower surface (except in floating aquatic plants) the epidermis is perforated by numerous stomata. The epidermis has a coating of wax called cuticle, which helps waterproof the leaf, helping it to retain water.

B. Stomata

1. Stomata are tiny pores found on the lower or under side of most leaves. Occasionally, stomata are found both on the lower and upper surface, especially in aquatic plants such as water lilies, corn and alfalfa. No stomata occur on submerged leaves of aquatic plants. Stomata permits gas exchange.

2. Stomata are bordered by guard cells. Guard cells are the only cells in epidermis that have chloroplasts. They function to control gas exchange and regulation of plant water content.

3. Guard cells expand or contract depending on light and water content, thereby opening or closing the stomata to regulate gas exchange and water loss.

4. Open stomata permit air flow into the leaf, providing the source of CO_2 used in photosynthesis. Air flow out of the stomata "excretes" O_2, produced by photosynthesis in leaves into the atmosphere along with water lost through transpiration.

C. Leaf Mesophyll

1. Mesophyll consists of the several cell layers that lie between upper and lower leaf surfaces. Mesophyll forms the interior part of the leaf where most photosynthesis occurs.

2. There are two distinct layers of mesophyll, palisade mesophyll and spongy mesophyll.

    a. Palisade mesophyll consists of the upper two layers of column-shaped parenchyma cells that contain 80% chlorophyll, where most leaf photosynthesis occurs.

    b. Spongy mesophyll, also called chlorenchyma, consists of loosely arranged parenchyma with abundant air spaces between cells. It also has chloroplasts for photosynthesis. This mesophyll is also found in stems of herbaceous plants.

D. Veins

1. Veins are bundles of vascular tissue that extend through the mesophyll.
2. A vein consists of xylem and phloem surrounded by fibers, the whole called a bundle sheath.
3. Veins are both the skeleton and the "plumbing" of a leaf. The xylem of veins brings water from roots, the phloem of veins redistributes food made by leaf mesophyll.
4. Monocots have parallel veins and mesophyll is not separated into palisade and spongy layers.
5. Some monocots have large, thin walled bulliform cells that border main vascular bundle. As the plant dries, these cells collapse causing the leaf to fold to reduce transpiration.

IV. Autumn Color Changes and Leaf Fall
A. Leaf Color Changes

1. Leaf color is mostly caused by pigments located in the chloroplasts. These color pigments include carotene (yellow), xanthophylls (pale yellow), anthocyanins (reds in acids & blue in basic aqueous solutions), and betacyanin (bright reds of flowers and fall leaves). Chlorophylls are by far the most abundant and produce the green colors of leaves.
2. During most of the seasons, leaves and stems are green because the chlorophyll pigments are so abundant that all other leaf pigments are masked by the bright hues of green.
3. In autumn as the leaves and other parts of the plant start to die, the chlorophyll pigments decompose first, exposing the colors of the other pigments. These decompose much more slowly since they give autumn colors to leaves.
4. Some plants exhibit only one color in leaves as breakdown occurs. Leaves of birches and ashes, for example are bright yellow as underlying xanthophylls show through.
5. Others, like maples and sumacs vary from locality to locality and even leaf-to-leaf depending on concentration of pigments present.

B. Leaf Fall

1. Plants that shed their leaves are called deciduous plants. The seasonal cycle begins with growth of new leaves in spring which are shed each fall. In fact, the name for fall is an old English name relating to the most spectacular event of that season, the fall of leaves.
2. In tropical and semitropical areas of the world leaf fall is related to wet and dry seasons.
3. The shedding of leaves is called abscission. Abscission occurs in an abscission zone located near the base of petiole. The abscission zone consists of several layers of cells.
4. During the growing season, young leaves produce a hormone called auxin, that prevents cell activity in the abscission layer.
   - a. Cold and wet conditions of autumn, reduce auxin output, stimulating the growth of abscission initials in the abscission zone.
   - b. Growth of abscission initials result in two distinct layers in the petiole, the protective layer and the separation layer.
     1. Protective layer is closest to the stem and several cell layers thick. As the leaf ages, it develops a suberin coating to protect the main stem after leaf fall.
     2. The separation layer develops on the leaf side. The cells of the separation layer swell, divide, and become gelatinous. Separation begins in response to temperature and/or photoperiod changes, lack of water, or damage to the leaf.
     3. This also provides a mechanism to discard damaged leaves.

V. Specialized Leaves
A. Leaves exhibit specializations in response to many different needs.

1. Shade leaves are plant leaves that occur in the shade part of plants. They are often thinner and have fewer hairs than leaves that occur in direct light. Shade leaves also are larger and have fewer well-defined mesophyll layers and fewer chloroplasts.
2. Succulent leaves are found in plants of arid regions. They are usually leathery with few stomata that are sunken below the surface of the leaf. Some succulent leaves have a dense, hairy covering to trap water droplets, others have several layers of epidermis.
3. Tendrils are specialized leaves that curl around structure and help hold plant in place. In peas, leaves are compound and tendrils are the end leaflets.

Tendrils function by rapid cell growth opposite side making contact, forming a spring like coil. Sclerenchyma cells develop that make contact area strong and flexible. In some plants like yellow vetchling, the whole leaf is modified tendril. In these leaves, photosynthesis occurs in stipules. In Clematis, the tendrils are actually the rachis of compound leaves.

4. Spines are modified leaves that protect the plant from herbivores. Spines are common in desert plants because their small surface area reduces water loss. In some woody plants, such as black locust and mesquite, the stipules of leaves actually form the spines. In plants like barberry, the entire leaf becomes the spine. The thorns of raspberries and roses are outgrowths of epidermis of the stem and not true spines.

5. Reproductive leaves produce new plants as leaf tips by growth, resulting in different generations of plants linked together. Examples of plants with reproductive leaves include walking ferns and air plants.

6. Floral leaves are specialized leaves found at the bases of flowers or flower stalks also called bracts. In Poinsettia and Dogwoods, the leaves resemble flower petals.

7. Insect-trapping leaves occur in about 200 species of plants. Most occur in swampy areas, bogs where soils are often deficient in nutrients. For example, nitrogen plants obtain nutrients by trapping insects with specially modified leaves.

   a. Pitcher Plants have normal leaves for photosynthesis, other leaves are shaped like a vase for trapping insects. These vase-shaped leaves emit a distinctive odor to attract insects from nectar-secreting glands located at the rim of the trap.

   (1) Insects attracted to the nectar slip and fall into a pool of fluid that forms within the interior basin formed by the pitcher leaf.

   (2) Stiff, downward pointing hairs keep trapped insects form escaping.

   (3) A pool of water at the bottom of the "pitcher" leaf contains enzymes that digest the drowned insects whose nutrients are absorbed.

   b. Sundew Plants are tiny plants with roundish leaves covered with several hundred glandular hairs that secrete sticky fluids on their surfaces. The droplets sparkle in the sun attracting insects which land on them and get stuck. Hairs bend inward and trap insects which are digested by enzymes secreted by the hairs.

   c. The insect trapping leaves of Venus Flytraps consist of two halves which fold inward to close like the jaws of a trap. Leaves are triggered when insects land on tiny hairs within the leaf. Leaf enzymes digest the trapped insects.

d. Bladderworts are plants with finely dissected leaves that float in shallow water. A stomach-shaped bladder with a trap door is located near the base of each leaf. If an insect touches hairs in the bladder, the trapdoor opens and water rushes into the bladder sweeping the insect out. The door then shuts behind to capture the insect.

VI. Commercial Value of Leaves
A. Leaves as Food and Drug Sources

1. Leaves of many plants such as cabbage, lettuce, spinach, and chard are important foods.
2. Leaves of many plants such as dill, bayberry, thyme, oregano are rich sources of spices.
3. Some of the many dyes extracted from leaves include yellow from barberry, and red from henna.
4. Cordage and fibers extracted from leaf fibers of plants such as Agave.
5. Oils in perfumes, oil of citronella as mosquito repellant, and medicinal oils such as Eucalyptus oil.
6. Drugs include cocaine from coca leaves, and atropine from deadly nightshade.
7. Tobacco consists of dried leaves, marijuana includes buds and dried leaves.
8. Beverages made from leaves include teas. Tequila is made by pulverizing the the leaves of the *Agave cactis*.

Multiple Choice Self-Test

_____ 1. Very pale yellow colors of leaves in fall are mostly caused by: (a) carotenes (b) xanthophylls (c) anthocyanins (d) proteins (e) chlorophyls.

_____ 2. Green color of leaves in spring is mostly caused by: (a) sunlight (b) proteins (c) chlorophyll (d) xanthophylls (e) all of the above.

_____ 3. The glands of leaves are located in the: (a) phloem (b) epidermis (c) xylem (d) palisade mesophyll (e) spongy mesophyll (f) guard cells.

_____ 4. These leaf cells have cutin impregnated in their outer walls: (a) epidermis (b) palisade layer (c) spongy layer (d) all of the above.

_____ 5. Leaves function primarily: (a) to produce food (b) to store food (c) to transport food (d) for protection (e) none of the above.

_____ 6. Bundles of xylem and phloem that extend into the leaves are called: (a) simple tissue (b) secretory tissue (c) veins (d) blades (e) rays.

_____ 7. Epidermal cells that regulate water loss and gas exchange are: (a) spongy tissue (b) palisade tissue (c) veins (d) rays (e) guard cells.

_____ 8. The pattern of distribution of vascular tissues in the leaf is termed: (a) rays (b) veination (c) vascular tissue (d) all of the above.

_____ 9. When guard cells are swollen or expanded the stomata are: (a) closed (b) open (c) neither (d) all of the above (e) none of the above.

Matching Self Test About Leaves

____ 1. Highest concentration of chlorophyll
____ 2. Leaf hairs are extensions of
____ 3. Openings in surface of leaves
____ 4. Protective waxy substance
____ 5. Leaf stalk is called a
____ 6. Passive control of water loss by leaves
____ 7. Active control of water loss by leaves
____ 8. Veins of a leaf are actually the?

a. stomata
b. epidermis
c. palisade parenchyma
d. petiole
e. vascular bundles
f. cuticle

Concepts Self-Test

1. Describe the mechanisms of leaf fall during autumn of each year. What are the functions of this annual leaf fall? Does it also occur in tropical plants in fall? At any other time of year?

Visual Self-Test

In the diagram of the leaf below label the following: upper epidermis, spongy mesophyll palisade mesophyll, guard cell, stomata, lower epidermis, vascular bundle, parenchyma

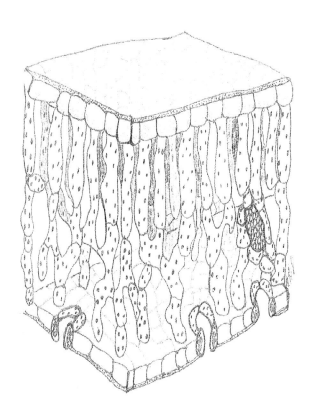

Chapter 8 Flowers, Fruits and Seeds

This Chapter considers the following questions:
➤ How do monocot and dicot flowers differ?
➤ What is the structure of male and female flowers?
➤ How is flower structure related to pollinations?
➤ What is the anatomy of a fruit and how are fruits classified?
➤ How are fruits and seeds dispersed?

I. Monocot and Dicot Flowers
A. Terminology and Types of Flowers
    1. Flowers are reproductive structures or bodies that take various forms to attract a pollinator to fertilize the ovary. They vary widely in size and form. The largest known flower is *Rafflesia* from Indonesia, which is a meter across and weighs over 7 kilograms.
    2. Plants produce flowers at specific times in their life cycle.
        a. Annuals complete their life cycle in one year.
        b. Biannuals complete their life cycle in two years, flowering only in the second year.
        c. Perennials complete their life cycle in several years, often flowering each year.

B. Differences between Dicots and Monocots
    1. Almost ¾ of all flowering plants are dicots. All flowering trees and shrubs are dicots.
    2. Dicot characteristics include
        (a) seed with two cotyledons
        (b) flower parts mostly in 4s or 5s or multiples of 4& 5
        (c) leaf with distinct network of veins
        (d) vascular cambium and frequently cork cambium present
        (e) vascular bundles of stem in ring
        (f) having pollen grains mostly with 3 apertures.
    3. Monocots are derived from dicots and include the lilies, grasses, orchids, irises and palms.
    4. Monocot characteristics include:
        (a) seed with one cotyledon

(b) flower parts in 3s or multiple of 3s.
(c) leaf with more or less parallel veins.
(d) vascular cambium and cork cambium absent.
(e) stem vascular bundles scattered.
(f) pollen grains mostly with one aperture.

II. The Structure of Flowers
A. Structure of Flowers

1. A flower is a modified leaf. It originates as a primordium on a stem containing growth meristems that develop into flower parts. The base of the flower to be develops into a peduncle. Thus, the peduncle becomes the base that supports the flower.

B. Flower Parts

1. The peduncle is the base of the flower that supports the floral structure. It swells into a pad to form a receptacle for the flower.
2. Outermost whorls of a flower consists of green, leaf-like sepals. Together the sepals form a structure called the calyx, which functions to protect the flower while it is in the bud.
3. Second whorl of the flower consists of petals which collectively are called the corolla. A showy corolla attracts pollinators, others have special markings invisible to the human eyes. But can be seen by insects, which can see in the ultraviolet range of light. The corolla is often missing in wind pollinated plants, an adaptation which facilitates pollination.
4. Inflorescence refers to the arrangement of flowers on the peduncle. In some plants such as lilacs and grapes, several flowers are clustered on small stalks (pedicels).

C. Reproductive Parts of the Flower

1. The pistil is the female part of the flower and occurs in the middle. It is often vase-like in shape and consists of three regions that merge with the peduncle.

   a. Stigma is the slight swelling at top that receives the pollen.
   b. Style is the slender stalk holding the stigma. It conducts the pollen to the ovary.
   c. The ovary is the swollen base of style which later becomes the fruit. The base of the ovary is attached to the peduncle and is called a receptacle.
2. There are two kinds of ovaries, superior and inferior.
   a. A superior ovary is located above the attachment of the receptacle.
   b. An inferior ovary is one in which the receptacle grows up around the ovary.

3. The ovary contains egg-shaped ovules which ultimately produce the egg. A fertilized egg becomes a seed.

4. Stamens are the male part of the flower. They are attached to the receptacle at the base of the pistil. A stamen consists of a filament called an anther that develops pollen grains.

III. Fruits
A. Introduction to Fruits

1. The fruit is an ovary that has developed and matured. It contains seeds.
2. Fruits include cherries, pears, apples, and peaches as well as many vegetables such as tomatoes, string beans, cucumbers and squashes.
3. All fruits arise from flowers and are found only in flowering plants.
4. All fruits must be fertilized, otherwise they wither and eventually drop off.
5. Fruits are fertilized by pollen grains which carry hormones, that initiate fruit development. As seeds within the fruit develop, they produce hormones for further fruit growth.

B. The Anatomy of Fruit

1. A fruit is divided into three regions: the exocarp, mesocarp and endocarp.
    a. The exocarp is the outer covering, or skin of the fruit.
    b. The endocarp is the inner boundary that forms around the seed. It may be hard as in a peach pit or papery as found in apples.
    c. The mesocarp refers to that part of the fruit between the endocarp and exocarp.
2. The pericarp is the collective term for the exocarp, mesocarp, and endocarp.

C. Types of Fruits

1. Fleshy fruits are fruits that are partly or mostly fleshy at maturity such as cherries.
2. Simple fleshy fruits such as drupes and pomes develop from a single pistil.

    a. Drupe is a fruit consisting of a single seed enclosed by hard stony endocarp or pit. Drupes usually develop from flowers with a superior ovary and a single ovule. The mesocarp may not always be fleshy as in coconuts, which has a fibrous husk. Drupes include apricots, cherries, peaches, plums, olives and almonds.
    b. A berry develops from a compound ovary and contains more than one seed. The entire pericarp of a berry is fleshy. It is often difficult to distinguish the mesocarp and endocarp of berries. There are three types of berries:

(1) True berry-one seeded forms include avocados and dates; multiple seeded forms are tomatoes, grapes, persimmons, and peppers. Many so-called berry plants are not berries (strawberry, raspberry, blackberry). Some berries are derived from flowers with inferior ovary, so other parts of ovary flower contributes to flesh. These can be identified by persistence of flower parts or scars at the tip (blueberries, pomegranates,cranberries, bananas).

(2) A pepo has a thick rind or exocarp. Examples of pepos include pumpkins, cucumbers, watermelons, squashes and cantaloupes.

(3) A hesperidium is a berry with leathery skin that contains oils. Outgrowths of the inner lining of ovary becomes sack-like and swollen with juice. Tangerines and kumquats.

c. Pomes are simple fleshy fruits comprised mostly of the enlarged receptacle that grows up around the ovary. The endocarp is papery or leathery. Examples include apples and pears. The apple core is the ovary. Most of the fruit is receptacle. Pomes, pepos, and some berries often referred to are accessory fruits. Because much of the flesh of the fruit derives from the accessory tissue.

3. Aggregate fruits are derived from a single flower with many pistils. Each pistil develops into tiny drupes or other fruitlets that remain in a cluster.

a. Some examples are raspberries, blackberries and strawberries.
b. In strawberries, the cone-shaped receptacle becomes fleshy and red. Each pistil becomes an achene with accessory tissue.

4. Multiple Fruits are derived from several to many flowers in a single inflorescence. Each flower has its own receptacle, but they all grow together in a single fruit at maturity. Mulberries, Osage oranges, pineapples and figs.

5. Dry fruits are fruits that have a dry rather than a fleshy mesocarp at maturity. There are two types:

a. Dry fruits that split at maturity are separated by the way they split.
(1) Follicle splits along one side only, exposing seeds within. Peony, larkspur, columbine, milkweed.
(2) Legumes split along two seams, e.g., peas, beans, lentils.
(3) Siliques split along two sides or seams but seeds are on a central partition which is exposed when two halves separate. Mustards such as broccoli, cabbage, radish.

(4) Capsules are most common dry fruits that split. Capsules have at least two carpals and split in various ways-along partitions between carpals, or split through cavities in carpals. Others form a cap that opens at one end when ripe. Still, other types of capsules form a row of pores through which the seeds are shaken out as the capsule rattles back and forth in the wind. Irises, lilies, orchids, poppies, violets

b. Dry fruits that do not split at maturity consist of a single seed that is fused or attached to the pericarp to varying degrees.

(1) Achene is a single seed attached to surrounding pericarp only at the base. Husk or pericarp is easily separated from seed.

(2) Nuts are one-seeded fruits similar to achenes but are generally larger and pericarp is much harder and thicker. Nuts develop a cup or cluster of bracts at base. Examples include hazelnuts, chestnuts, acorns, and hickory nuts. Many so called nuts are not nuts, e.g., peanuts are legumes, coconuts, almonds, walnuts, pecans, cashews, and pistachios are actually drupes rather than nuts.

(3) Grain (caryopsis)- the pericarp of grain is tightly fused to the seed and cannot be separated from it. All members of the grass family such as corn, wheat, oats, and barley.

(4) Samara is a pericarp around a seed that extends out in form of wings or membrane to aid dispersal. Maples, ashes, and tree-of-heaven.

(5) Schizocarp is a twin fruit that splits into two one seeded segments when dry, e.g., parsley, carrots, anise, caraway and dill.

IV. Dispersal of Fruits and Seeds
A. Wind Dispersal

1. Seeds dispersed by wind have special structures to enhance drifting in the wind stream.
2. The samara of maples causes fruit to spin and be carried on the wind. The hop hornbeam seed is inside an inflated sac which makes it light and buoyant. In buttercups, sunflowers and dandelions, the seeds have parachute like plumes.
3. Round seeds of button snakeroot and Jerusalem sage roll along the ground when driven by winds.

4. Tiny seeds carried in wind drifts; for example orchids and heaths.
5. Tumbleweed is an example of an entire plant that is rolled along in the wind.

B. Dispersal by Animals

1. Many types of seeds are dispersed by animals (burdock, stick tights)
2. Shorebirds carry seeds in mud that cakes on their feet.
3. Many birds and mammals eat fruits and seeds which pass unharmed through digestive tracts. Enzymes of host intestine partially digest exocarp so seed can germinate.
4. Some seeds are stored or placed in caches by birds and small mammals. Uneaten seeds may germinate.
5. Many fruits and seeds have devices that attach to host which effectively disperses the seed, e.g., burdock, bedstraw, bur clover. Some seeds have tiny hooks (tickseeds and stick tights), other seeds are sticky (flax and twinflower). Some have oils to attract ants (Bleeding hearts and trillium).

C. Dispersal by Water

1. Some seeds are dispersed by waters of rivers, streams, currents of lakes and ponds. These seeds float because they contain trapped air (coconuts, sedges, water lilies).
2. Some seeds dispersed by water have waxy outer surface that promote floating.
3. Heavy downpour of rain will cause floods and uproot plants on stream bank.
4. Large raindrops splash seeds out in the opened capsules.

D. Other Dispersal Mechanisms

1. Some seeds are mechanically ejected from capsules (witch hazel, jewelweed).
2. In some pumpkins, seeds are squirted out of the end of the melon like fruits.
3. Humans deliberately or not are greatest dispersal agents of seeds.
    a. Examples of deliberate dispersal include crop plants such as potatoes and corn, both of which were transported from the New World and introduced into the Old World. African Grass, Orchard Grass, most clovers transported as pasture grasses from Old World to New World with pioneers.
    b. Examples of inadvertent dispersal include our most noxious weed and other pest species (Oriental bittersweet vine, barberry, Kudzu, various thistles, Japanese rose).

V. Seeds
A. Structure of Seeds

1. Structure of kidney beans provides a good example of seed structure.

2. The hilum is a white scar on concave side where ovule was attached to the ovary wall.
3. The micropyle is a small "dot-like" structure adjacent to hilum, where the pollen entered.
4. The two halves of the bean are called cotyledons and are used for food storage.
5. The embryo is the tiny plant to which cotyledons are attached.
6. The plumule is the meristem at one end of the embryo. Cotyledons attach just below the plumule.
7. The epicotyl is the stem part of the axis above the cotyledons.
8. The hypocotyls is the stem part of the axis below the cotyledons.
9. The radicle represents the root end of the little plant.
10. The endosperm is found in some seeds (corn) for food storage.
11. The coleoptile is the tubular sheath containing the plumule.
12. The coleorhiza is the tubular sheath containing the radicle.

B. Germination of Seeds
1. Germination is promoted by optimum temperature and soil water content in most plants.
2. In woody plants in temperate regions, germination occurs only after cold temperatures.

C. Dormancy of Seeds
1. Refers to how long seeds can survive before germination. In many plants, the period of dormancy is genetically controlled. But in some, dormancy can be induced by adverse climatic or environmental factors.
2. Dormancy is an adaptation that enhances survival of seed during harsh climatic, environmental, and other conditions.
3. Emergence from dormancy may be stimulated in several different ways in plants.
4. Some plants have seeds that emerge from dormancy to germinate by exposure to light.
5. Legumes and other plants have thick seed coats that must mechanically be abraded by wet and cold or freezing and thawing conditions, to stimulate seed emergence from dormancy.
6. Other seeds, require freezing and thawing induced movements of soil and rocks to thin seed coat sufficiently; before water can be absorbed and germinate, a process called scarification.
7. Some seeds have substances in their coat that inhibits growth and must be washed away before seed activation can occur. This process is known as stratification.

D. Seed Longevity
1. Longevity of seeds varies greatly from a few days or weeks (cottonwoods, willows, orchids) to several thousand years (Arctic lupines may germinate after being frozen for 10,000 years). Seeds buried 4500 years ago buried in the graves of the ancient pharaohs of Egypt were found to be viable.

Matching Self-Test
Match the flower type with its most likely form, pollination or pollinator

____ 1. Small, white, and smelly flowers?   A. wind
____ 2. Flowers that lack sepals and petals: B. moths
____ 3. Flowers that smell like rotting flesh?   C. flies
____ 4. Flowers that are yellow and bloom at night?   D. hummingbirds
____ 5. Long, tubular flowers   E. bees

Matching Self-Test
Match the fruit with its description

____ 1. Members of the pumpkin family   a. drupes
____ 2. Dates and avocados   b. true berries
____ 3. Tangerines, other citrus fruits   c. pepos
____ 4. Acorns   d. pomes
____ 5. Pineapples and figs   e. hesperidiums
____ 6. Apricots   f. legumes
____ 7. Apples and pears   g. aggregate fruits
____ 8. Peas and beans   h. nuts

Multiple Choice Self-Test

____ 1. Best source of plant sperm for a cross pollination experiment: (a) sepals (b) petals (c) anters (d) pollen (e) spores (f) ovaries
____ 2. Ornamental gingko trees are usually male because: (a) female trees bear a heavy scent of rotten flesh to attract flies for pollination (b) female trees are only 5 feet tall (c) male trees have an attractive scent (d) all of the above.
____ 3. Plants that have a complete life cycle in a single year are called: (a) biannuals (b) annuals (c) therophytes (d) monocots (e) dicots
____ 4. The skin of a fruit is termed: (a) carpel (b) endocarp (c) mesocarp (d) exocarp (e) pericarp (f) all of the above.

_____ 5. The stamens and petals attach to: (a) ovary (b) receptacle (c) calyx
(d) peduncle (e) ovule (f) stem (g) leaf

_____ 6. The wing of a samara comes from the: (a)   stipule (b) pericarp (c) sepal
(d) ovary (e) ovule (f) all of the above.

_____ 7. The female part of a flower: (a) pistil (b) peduncle (c) ovary (d) stigma
(e) all of the above (f) none of the above.

_____ 8. The fleshy part of a fruit is typically: (a) exocarp (b) endocarp (c) mesocarp
(d) all of the above (e) none of the above.

_____ 9. This type of fruit develops from a compound ovary: (a) nut (b) acorn
(c) mesocarp (d) berry (e) drupe (f) pome

_____10. These seeds split along two sides or seams: (a) pome (b) silique (c) drupe
(d) legume (e) follicle (f) all of the above.

_____11. These seeds split into two-seeded segments when dry: (a) samara (b) nut
(c) grain (d) achene (e) capsule

_____12. The food storage part of seeds is termed the: (a) capsule (b) cotyledon
(c) plumule (d) coleorhiza (e) all of the above.

Concepts Self-Test

1. Most people think that plants are immobile or nearly so. After all, unlike humans, plants grow only in one place throughout their life. If we take the position that dispersal is an essential attribute of all living organisms then what mechanisms do plants use to disperse?

2. What is the relationship between size, color, ripening, and maturation of fruit and how might this operate as a natural visual signal? In other words, why should it matter if an animal takes a green apple or a red apple?

3. Are ornamental street trees and yardscape trees usually male or female? Why?

4. How do we distinguish between a fruit and a vegetable?

Matching Self-Test

_____ 1. Fruits with wings such as samaras   a. wind dispersed
_____ 2. Round seeds of Jerusalem Sage   b. animal dispersed
_____ 3. Tiny seeds of orchids   c. water dispersed
_____ 4. Seeds with tiny hooks.   d. gravity dispersed
_____ 5. Seeds with waxy coating for floating
_____ 6. Seeds with air trapped inside

Visual Self-Test

Label the following floral parts: pistil, stamens, anther, pollen grains, pollen tube, Ovary, ovule, pollen tube, style, filament, receptacle.

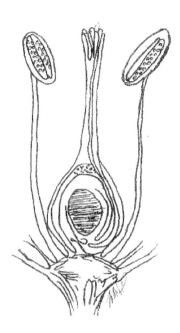

Visual Self-Test

Label the apple core: pericarp, pith, calyx, stamen, seed, skin, vascular bundle.

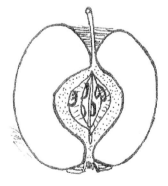 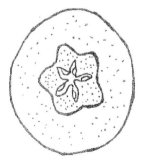

Visual Self-Test

Label the following parts of the corn seed: seed coat, ovary wall, aleurone layer, cotyledon, coleoptile, radicle, coleorhiza

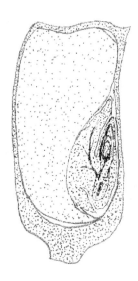
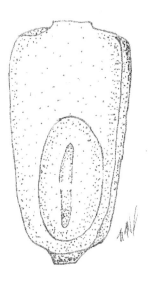

Chapter 9 Water, Minerals and Soil

This chapter considers the following questions:
➢ How does water move into and through plants?
➢ How does phloem transport food?
➢ What are the basic properties of soil that are important to plants?
➢ What soil nutrients are needed by plants?

I. Water and Plants
A. Concepts about Water
1. The constant flow of water into and out of plants must be regulated for transport, metabolic purposes and controlled to prevent water loss or desiccation.
2. Diffusion is movement of molecules from areas of greater concentration to areas of lesser concentration, so that they are evenly distributed through space.
3. Osmosis is diffusion of water through a permeable or semi-permeable cell membrane.
   a. Osmotic potential is the pressure required to keep osmosis from occurring. As water enters the cell, its walls can't expand any further and the cell becomes turgid.
   b. Turger pressure refers to the water pressure exerted against the cell walls.
4. Plasmolysis refers to the movement of water out of cell due to a change in pressure gradient.
5. Imbibitions is the process by which water is absorbed by hydrophilic substances that attract water. Water is attracted to the surfaces of a hydrophilic substance.

B. Water Movement Through Plants
1. Most (95%) of water moving through plant is lost through evaporation from leaf air spaces and stomata. Another 5% escapes through the cuticle.
2. Plant water loss is called **transpiration**. A corn plant transpires 4 gallons of water in a week. An acre of corn can transpire 350,000 gallons of water in a 100 day growing season.
2. Water enters plant roots via osmosis, then enters xylem tubes by root pressure and transported up the xylem via cohesion-tension theory.
3. Root pressure results from osmotic intake of water into roots. Water basically enters the root tissue following a concentration gradient and is driven into

the xylem. As water continues to enter the root tissue (being absorbed from surrounding soil) it exerts a root pressure force on the water already in xylem, pushing it upwards.

4. The Cohesion-Tension Theory- evaporation of water from leaf surfaces creates a pulling force on water below. Water molecules adhere to each other and vessel walls. As water evaporates from leaf mesophyll, cells adjacent water molecules are "pulled" along via cohesion-tension all along the length of the xylem tubes. Thus transpiration produces a pull or tension on water columns in the plant. This water tension will move water all the way to the top of a tall tree. Any breaking of the water column produces a gas bubble. This a block which the plant eventually repairs by reabsorption.

II. Transport of Food in Phloem
A. Water helps transport food in phloem.
1. Food transport in water solution of phloem is also called translocation.
2. Food is transported in sieve tubes of phloem while being transported.
3. Movement is up to 100 centimeters per hour (much more rapid than possible by diffusion).

B. Pressure Flow Hypothesis of Food Transport in Phloem
1. Current theory to explain how food is transported in phloem.
2. This theory suggests that food flows from a source where water is absorbed by osmosis to a sink such as leaves, where food is used. Food is transported along a concentration gradient.
3. Phloem Loading occurs by active transport and involves several steps.
   a. Sugar is taken up by active transport into root cells. Water enters in response to increased sugar concentrations, which decreases water content; therefore water enters by osmosis.
   b. Entry of water changes turgid pressure (causing cell to swell), this drives fluid through sieve tube towards leaves. As sugar is actively removed from phloem, tubes in leaves water follows and osmotic pressure declines.
   c. Most of the water eventually is returned to the xylem to be transpired.

C. How Transpiration is Regulated
1. Stomata regulate transpiration, water loss, and gas exchange via activity of guard cells.
2. Guard cells have elastic walls and are shaped like sausage balloons joined end-to-end.
3. Stomata open and close due to changes in turgor pressure in guard cells.
4. Pore closes when turgor pressure is low and opens when turgor pressure is high.

5. Turgor pressure changes as osmosis and active transport occur between guard cells and epidermal cells around them via ion exchange.

    a. Ion exchange occurs as guard cells take up potassium and chloride ions or starch from other cells via active transport. Osmosis results in water entry into guard cells, making them turgid and opening stomata. At night, photosynthesis stops, ion and organic content decreases, water no longer flows into guard cells via osmosis, and they shrink, causing the stomata to close.

    b. Chemical control- stomata can also be controlled chemically via hormone called abscisic acid which is produced in leaves subject to water stress.

D. Stomata Specializations

1. The stomata of most plants open during day and close.
2. To conserve water, stomata of many desert plants open at night and close during day to conserve water evaporation during the hot, dry, desert days.
3. Some plants have a special type of photosynthesis called CAM photosynthesis. Their stomata open at night to acquire CO_2, for use in photosynthesis when stomata are closed.
4. Some desert plants have sunken stomata covered by epidermal hairs to reduce water loss.

E. Guttation

1. If a cool night follows a warm, humid day, water droplets produced through structures called hydathodes at tips of veins in some plants. This form of water loss is called guttation.
2. Guttation resembles dew but actually forms as a result of root pressure.
3. As water evaporates, it may leave a residue of salt concentrates and organic substance which can be harvested. MSG- monosodium glutamate in Accent, a flavor enhancer.

IV. Soils and Plants
A. Properties of Soils

1. Soils are part of a crust varying in thickness.
2. Soils are comprised of many ingredients---sand, rocks, pebbles, silt, clay, humus, dead leaves, twigs, organic matter, roots, small animals, bacteria, air and water.
3. Pore spaces within soil hold water and air and determine how well soil is aerated and drained.
4. Soils have a distinct structure. They are subdivided into regions called horizons

    a. O Horizon is the leaf litter horizon distinguished by accumulation of organic debris.

b. A Horizon is the uppermost layer of topsoil where leaf litter decomposes into humus, then mineralizes. Minerals are leached from this horizon downward to B Horizon.

c. B Horizon is the horizon where minerals leached from A horizon accumulate. Plant roots penetrate to this horizon to absorb the minerals in water.

d. C Horizon is the transition from soil to parent material beneath the soil such as bedrock.

5. Living Organisms and Organic Composition—living organisms comprise about 1/1000 weight of soil (about 1 kilogram per acre). Bacteria and fungi present in soil decompose organic matter. Animals cultivate soil by burrowing and other activities. Animal wastes and dead bodies add to nutriments of soil.

6. Organic Composition-average topsoil is about 25% air, 25% water, 48% minerals and 2% organic matter. Wetland soils has almost no microbial activity, therefore little decomposition occurs.

7. Soil texture refers to the size of the individual soil particles. Sand silt-clay.

a. Sands and gravels are composed of small particles chemically bound together.

b. Silt consists of particles that are mostly too small to be seen without lens.

c. Clay consists of tiny particles, occurs as individual particles called micelles. These are sheet-like, negatively charged and held together by chemical bonds. Clay micelles attract, exchange or retain positively charged mineral ions.

8. Soil structure refers to arrangement of soil particles into groups or aggregates.

a. Agricultural soils are granular soils with pore spaces that occupy 40-60% of total soil volume. Pores contain air and water, which provide spaces for soil organisms.

b. Clay soils have very small pores that restrict water, air content and movement.

c. Sandy soils have large pores that drain by gravity. The movement of water through sandy soils leaches nutrients out, leaving them sterile.

B. Water in Soils

1. Water in soils is absolutely necessary for plants, but too much water leaches out minerals and may result in water-logged soils that kill roots.

2. Soil water occurs in three forms-hygroscopic water, gravitational water, capillary water.

a. Hygroscopic water is physically bound to soil particles and unavailable to plants.

b. Gravitational water drains out of pore spaces following rain.

c. Capillary water refers to water that occurs in soil pores.
3. Following drainage, the water remaining in soils is called the field capacity of the soil. Field capacity is controlled by soil texture and organic materials that attract water. Plants can absorb water when it is at or near field capacity level. As soil dries, the water around each particle shrinks until it is unable to be tapped by root. If no water is added to the soil, the plant eventually wilts. Soil is then at permanent wilting point.
4. pH of soil-affects soil and plants growing in it. Acid or alkaline soils may be toxic to roots. As alkalinity increases, many minerals are bound chemically and not available to plants.

C. Mineral Requirement for Growth

1. Some of the known essential elements of plant growth include C H O P K N S Ca Fe Mg Na Cl Cu
2. Mineral nutrients fall under two categories, macronutrients and micronutrients.
    a. Macronutrients include carbon, phosphorous, nitrogen, calcium, and sodium.
    b. Micronutrients are needed in small amounts, e.g., magnesium.
3. If soil is deficient in macronutrients or micronutrients, plant growth and function is impaired.

D. Mineral Use in Plants

1. Nitrogen is an essential component of amino acids that comprise proteins and nucleic acids such as adenine, cytosine, guanine, thymine, and uracil that comprises DNA and RNA molecules. Nitrogen is also an essential component of all cell ATP energy molecules. Lack of nitrogen (nitrogen deficiency) causes stunted growth and yellowing of leaves.
2. Magnesium is the major mineral component of chlorophyll. Each chlorophyll molecule contains four atoms of magnesium. A magnesium deficiency causes browning of plants which eventually die. Magnesium is also a component of certain plant enzymes.
3. Phosphate is another important component of amino acids, nucleic acids, and ATP energy molecules. Phosphate molecules form the backbone of DNA and RNA molecules. The high energy bonds of ATP are due to the coupling of phosphate molecules. Most plant fertilizers such as potash, contain high amounts of phosphate along with added amounts of nitrogen.
4. A deficiency of phosphate in soil results in stunted growth and purple veined leaves.
5. Potassium is important in control of stomata opening and closing and also functions as an enzyme cofactor. Yellow leaves often indicate potassium deficiency in soils.

6. Sulfur is an important binding atom that helps maintain the tertiary structure of plant and animal proteins. A deficiency of soil sulfur produces black spotting of leaves. The black spots are actually dead leaf tissue.

7. Most of the micronutrients such as copper, molybdenum, manganese, and iron are required in only small amounts but are absolutely necessary for plant function, growth and reproduction. Most micronutrients function as enzyme cofactors.

    a. Iron is a component of the cytochrome molecules that are part of the electron transport system which produces ATP molecules.

    b. Boron helps regulate the enzymatic breakdown of carbohydrates.

Multiple Choice Self-Test

_____ 1. Feeding the leaves of Venus flytrap plant fertilizer will satisfy the plant's need for: (a) water (b) carbon (c) nitrogen (d) oxygen.

_____ 2. A pale or white plant growing beneath trees is probably: (a) a mutant (b) a plant that uses colorless pigments (c) a plant that only carries out the dark reactions of photosynthesis (d) a plant that produces energy via fermentation (e) a parasitic plant.

_____ 3. Movement of water in the xylem: (a) involves active transport (b) is caused in part by evapotranspiration from the leaf surface (c) involves consumption of ATP (d) all of the above.

_____ 4. The mechanism by which sucrose enters a phloem sieve-tube cell: (a) active transport (b) osmosis (c) interaction of auxin.

_____ 5. Tiny particles called micelles make up this type of soil: (a) clay (b) sand (c) gravel (d) silt (e) all of the above.

_____ 6. Unaltered rock base of soil is termed: (a) A Horizon (b) B horizon (c) regolith (d) O Horizon (e) zone of leaching.

_____ 7. Plant mineral requirement important in regulating opening and closing of stomata: (a) iron (b) calcium (c) potassium (d) all of the above.

_____ 8. Water droplets produced by hydathodes is called: (a) guttation (b) dewdrops (c) evaporation (d) transpiration (e) all of the above.

_____ 9. This hormone also exerts chemical control of stomata: (a) guard cells (b) absisic acid (c) adrenalin (d) ascorbic acid (e) acetic acid.

Matching Self-Test

_____ 1. Production of chlorophyll   a. nitrogen

_____ 2. Formation of cell wall   b. molybdenum

_____ 3. Production of amino acids   c. carbon

_____ 4. Fixation of nitrogen   d. phosphorous

_____ 5. Formation of nucleic acids   e. iron

Matching Self-Test

____ 1. Water that is physically bound to soil particles
____ 2. Water that drains out of pore spaces
____ 3. Water that fills soil pores
____ 4. Water held in field after drainage
____ 5. Water leaches to this horizon
____ 6. Water leaches minerals to this horizon
____ 7. Plants lose water via this process

a. evapotranspiraton
b. hygroscopic water
c. capillary water
d. gravitational water
e. B horizon
f. A horizon
g. field capacity

Concepts Self-Test

1. Exactly what mechanisms promote the movement of water from soil through the plant and out of the leaves at the top of the tree, perhaps 300 feet high?

Visual Self-Test

Use the diagram presented below to illustrate by means of arrows and appropriate labeling the movements and reservoirs of water, minerals, and gases.

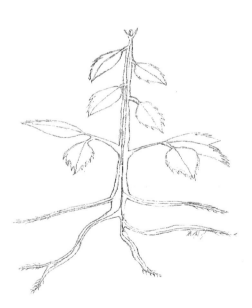

Chapter 10 Photosynthesis and Respiration

This chapter concentrates on the following questions:
- ➢ What are the energy sources for cells?
- ➢ What are the major events of photosynthesis?
- ➢ What are the major events of respiration?
- ➢ How is metabolic energy used in plants?

I. Energy and Plants
A. Introduction
   1. All living cells require energy to survive and energy to reproduce, grow and do work. Photosynthesis (provides energy) and Respiration (uses energy) are the two processes used to run the cell.
   2. Photosynthesis may be the single most important chemical reaction in the civilized world. It is the sole means of supporting life and produces oxygen, traps solar energy and enables plants to live. Despite large biomass of land plants much photosynthesis occurs in the ocean.
   3. Photosynthesis is the process whereby leaves, stems and other green parts of plants convert the kinetic energy of sunlight into the chemical energy of sugar the molecule.

II. Components of Photosynthesis
A. Carbon Dioxide
   1. Carbon dioxide comprises 0.035% of atmosphere along with 79% nitrogen and 20% oxygen.
   2. Carbon dioxide enters the leaf mesophyll by diffusion through stomata.

B. Water
   1. Less than 1% of the water in plants is used in photosynthesis by means of O_2 source.

C. Light
   1. Light reaches the earth in form of waves. The shortest waves are X-rays while the longer ones are radio waves. About 40% of this radiant energy is in the form of visible light.
   2. When passed through a prism, visible light breaks up into different wave lengths represented by colors. The shortest colors are violet and the largest reds. Other colors fall in the middle.

3. Most light used in photosynthesis is in the violet-blue and red-orange portion of the spectrum, the rest is reflected (that is why plants are green).
4. Amount and rate of photosynthesis is controlled by light and also by available CO_2. A shortage of either will reduce the process.
5. Excess light can cause photo-respiration which is a special process whereby cell uses oxygen and releases CO_2.
6. Excess light may also cause photo-oxidation, the destruction of chlorophyll molecules.

D. Pigments for Photosynthesis
1. Chlorophyll- there are several types which contain a single molecule of magnesium. Each chlorophyll molecule has a liquid tail that anchors molecule to the walls of thylakoids.
    a. Chlorophyll A is a bluish green color, which comprises about 75% of plant chlorophyll.
    b. Chlorophyll B is yellowish green in color and comprises about 25% of all plant chlorophyll in green plants.
2. Chlorophyll B absorbs light and transfers its energy to chlorophyll A. Thus chlorophyll B enables plants to gather light energy over a wide spectrum of light than just chlorophyll A.
3. Other chlorophylls such as Chlorophyll C and D take the place of B in some algae.
4. In each chloroplast, 250-400 chlorophyll molecules are grouped as a light harvesting unit called a photosynthetic unit. Many of these photosynthetic units are located in each grana.

III. Events of Photosynthesis
A. Light Reactions of Photosynthesis
1. Light reactions involve harvesting of light energy by chloroplasts.
2. Energy from light reactions split water molecules apart, producing hydrogen ions and electrons and oxygen gas. This is the oxygen that plants release into the atmosphere.
3. There are two types of Photosystems involved in photosynthesis.
    a. Photo-system I consists of 200 or more molecules of chlorophyll A and a small amount of chlorophyll B plus carotenoid pigments plus a special reaction-center molecule of chlorophyll A called pigment 700. This reaction center is where photons of light are absorbed. Remaining photo system pigments are called **antenna pigments** because together they function like an antenna which collects light for the reaction-center molecule.
    b. Photosystem II consists of molecules of chlorophyll A, B, and carotene attached to a reaction center molecule of chlorophyll called pigment 680.

4. When a photon of light strikes the Photosystem II, P680 the energy boosts an electron to a higher level, ultimately being used to split the water molecules into hydrogen and oxygen. The splitting of the water molecules is controlled by enzymes on the inside wall of the thylakoid membrane and the reaction is called photolysis.

B. Dark Reactions of Photosynthesis

1. The dark reactions take place outside the grana in the stroma of the chloroplasts using the products of light reactions. The dark reactions are also known as the Calvin Cycle.
2. In the dark reactions the CO_2 from the air is combined with a 5-carbon sugar and converted through several steps to 6-carbon sugars such as glucose. Energy is furnished by ATP and NADPH+H+ from light reaction.
3. Some of the produced sugars are recycled and other are stored as starch.
4. The 4-carbon Pathway is found in some tropical plants. 4-carbon pathway plants function at higher temperatures than 3-carbon plants and have higher rates of photosynthetic.
5. CAM Photosynthesis is also called Crassulacean acid metabolism, which is found in 20 plant families including cacti, stonecrop, orchids, bromeliads and many succulents growing in high light intensity. Plants in this group do not have well defined palisade layer in their leaves.
   a. CAM photosynthesis is similar to the C-4 cycle except that malic acid accumulates in chlorenchyma tissues at night and is converted to CO_2 during the day. This arrangement allows plants to function in conditions of low water and high light.

IV. Respiration
A. General Information

1. Respiration is the process of converting stored energy into energy to power cell activities.
2. Respiration is an energy releasing process that takes place in all active cells 24 hours a day.
3. Respiration begins in the cytoplasm adjacent to the mitochondria. It is completed within the mitochondria.
4. Respiration consists of systematically and enzymatically disassembling a sugar molecule. Oxygen is consumed and water, carbon dioxide, and ATP molecules are produced.
5. There are two types of respiration: anaerobic (without oxygen) and aerobic (with oxygen). In aerobic respiration, oxygen is consumed and in anaerobic respiration fermentation of oxygen is not required. Energy released in respiration is stored in ATP energy molecules.
6. Events of respiration include glycolysis, Krebs Citric Acid Cycle, and the Electron System.

B. Glycolysis

1. Glycolysis is an anaerobic event that takes place on the surface of the mitochondria membrane.
2. Input in glycolysis is a six-carbon molecule of glucose.
3. Glycolysis begins when a molecule of glucose is combined with phosphate to form Glucose 6-Phosphate, by a process called phosphorylation.
4. In a series of steps, a 6 carbon glucose splits into two 3-carbon molecules of pyruvic acid.
5. The net energy gain from glycolysis is 2 ATP molecules.

C. Krebs's Citric Acid Cycle

1. The Krebs's Citric Acid Cycle occurs inside mitochondria.
2. The basic ingredients include the pyruvic acid molecules produced during glycolysis.
3. First, each pyruvic acid molecule is enzymatically prepared by converting it into a molecule of acetyl coenzyme A which is then introduced into the Krebs's Citric Acid Cycle.
4. In a series of enzyme-mediated steps, the molecule is transferred from one citric acid to another. The last citric acid along the cycle is called oxalacetic acid-it bonds with an entering acetyl coenzyme A molecule to start the cycle again.
5. As the molecule is transferred from one citric acid to citric hydrogen atoms, water and carbon dioxide molecules are removed.
6. Products of the Krebs's Acid Cycle include water, hydrogen atoms, 2 ATP molecules and CO_2.
7. The CO_2 and water molecules are waste products, the hydrogen atoms are transported by NADH and FADH carrier molecules—still within the mitochondria—to enter the last event of respiration which is termed the Electron Transport System.

D. Electron Transport System

1. This final process in cell energy production is aerobic and occurs within the mitochondria.
2. The initial input into the Electron Transport System are the hydrogen atoms, carried as the hydrogen attached to NADH and FADH. These hydrogen atoms were stripped from the carbon molecule during the Krebs's Citric Acid Cycle.
3. Energy is extracted from the electrons of the hydrogen atoms and used to make ATP energy molecules via a process called chemiosmosis.
4. The final products of the Electron Transport System are ATP energy molecules and water.
5. During chemiosmosis, electrons provide the energy to pump hydrogen ions through an inner membrane within the mitochondria, creating a

concentration gradient in which more hydrogen ions are on the inside of the membrane compared to the outside.

6. The "diffusion" of hydrogen ion back through permeable channels in the membrane produces energy that is used to synthesize ATP molecules.

7. This process is called chemiosmosis, because the chemicals are diffusing across a membrane. Again, the chemicals that are diffusing are the hydrogen ions that were stripped from the original glucose molecule during the glycolysis and the Krebs's Citric Acid Cycle.

E. ATP Energy Molecules

1. In the cell there are special molecules that are high energy phosphate compounds called ATP.

2. Each ATP molecule is comprised of a molecule of adenine, glucose and three phosphoric acids.

3. Energy released from respiration is captured to form ATP from ADP and P molecules.

4. The energy binding the third P molecule to ADP is a high energy bond that can be broken with a single enzyme. Thus, ATP provides all of the energy needs of the cell to do work.

5. Each molecule of glucose cell respiration yields a net gain of 36 molecules of ATP.

V. Anaerobic Respiration and Fermentation

1. Fermentation does not require oxygen, so therefore is anaerobic.

2. Fermentation occurs in many bacteria, yeast, and other organisms that are anaerobes.

3. Basically, fermentation is equivalent to glycolysis, whose products are energy and alcohols.

4. Because sugars are not completely broken down as in respiration, fermentation is very inefficient as an energy production source. It is used by organisms in oxygen poor environment.

VI. Comparing Photosynthesis and Respiration
A. Photosynthesis Summary

1. Summary of events includes:

    (a) stores energy in sugar molecules.

    (b) uses carbon dioxide and water.

    (c) increases biomass of plants.

    (d) uses light energy to manufacture sugar molecules.

    (e) occurs only in cells containing chlorophyll.

    (f) produces oxygen in green plants and photosynthetic bacteria.

B. Respiration Summary

1. Summary of events in respiration includes:

(a) releases energy from sugar molecules.

(b) water and CO2 are released as by products.

(c) respiration occurs in either light or darkness.

(d) respiration occurs in all living cells of all living organisms.

(e) respiration occurs in cytoplasm (glycolysis) and in the mitochondria.

(f) respiration consumes oxygen in aerobic respiration.

(g) respiration produces ATP energy molecules.

(h) respiration generates metabolic water.

Multiple Choice Self Test

_____ 1. Water loss during photosynthesis is controlled by: (a) cuticle (b) pericycle (c) stomata (d) guard cells (e) all of the above (f) none of the above.

_____ 2. The sugar products of photosynthesis are distributed via the: (a) phloem (b) xylem (c) epidermis (d) pericycle (e) Casparian strip.

_____ 3. The carbon part of sugars synthesized during photosynthesis comes from: (a) water (b) sugar (c) carbon dioxide (d) starch (e) cellulose.

_____ 4. The hydrogen part of sugars fixed by photosynthesis comes from: (a) water (b) carbon dioxide (c) nitrogen oxide (d) cellulose (e) starch.

_____ 5. Which provides the most energy during respiration? (a) carbohydrates (b) waxes (c) fatty acids (d) proteins (e) nucleic acids (f) amino acids.

_____ 6. Which is not part of aerobic respiration in green plants? (a) chemiosmosis (b) glycolysis (c) electron transport chain (d) Kreb's citric acid cycle.

_____ 7. Which of the following involves anaerobic respiration: (a) fermentation (b) glycolysis (c) production of pyruvate (d) all of the above..

_____ 8. Components of a photosystem include: (a) a single group of chlorophyll molecules (b) single chlorophyll a molecule (c) mitochondria.

_____ 9. Colors of light used most often by photosynthesizing plants: (a) red, white and blue (b) red, blue, and violet (c) green and yellow (d) all colors (e) ultraviolet red (f) orange, green, and yellow.

_____ 10. In C4 plants: (a) light energy is stored in chloroplasts (b) water is stored in the stem and leaves (c) CO_2 is fixed and stored in the leaves (d) water and oxygen are stored in the roots (e) all of the above are true.

Glossary of Terms

Calvin Cycle. The dark reactions that occur during photosynthesis. In this cycle, which is sometimes called the Calvin-Benson cycle, carbon dioxide is combined with a sugar. The cycle is called the dark reactions or dark cycle because light is not needed as an energy source to complete the events of the Calvin Cycle.

Respiration. The fragmentation (oxidation) of glucose and other organic molecules to produce ATP, water, and carbon dioxide that occurs in all cells. Respiration consists of three processes: (1) glycolysis (2) Kreb's citric acid cycle, and (3) electron transport chain.

Chemiosmosis. Transfer of hydrogen electrons along electron transport system. In the process, high energy protons (the hydrogen atoms) are pumped across the mitochondrial membrane. Following a concentration gradient, they diffuse back through the membrane, promoting ATP generation.

Fermentation . Anaerobic (without oxygen) production of ATP similar to glycogen.

Photosynthesis. Sunlight driven production of glucose and other complex organic molecules. Inputs include energy from sunlight, carbon dioxide, and water. Evolution of atmospheric oxygen is a byproduct of photosynthesis

Understanding Concepts

1. Chemiosmosis is part of the Electron Transport Chain. Answer the following questions regarding the substrates and products of this respiration event.

> What is being transported in the Electron Transport Chain _____
> Where does the H come from _____
> What is the relationship between H and the Electron Transport Chain ____
> What is the relationship between protons and H_____
> What is the final acceptor of protons _____
> Where does the energy come from to synthesize ATP from ADP?_____
> Products of the Electron Transport Chain include_____

2. Compare inputs and products of photosynthesis and respiration. Where does the energy of sunlight ultimately end up in a working, functioning cell?

3. Take 3 molecules of glucose and reduce them to carbon dioxide, water, and ATP. How many units of ATP are consumed during the process and how many are produced?

Visualizing and Diagramming Concepts

Use the illustration below and sketch out the key events that occur during chemiosmosis.
Number the events and indicate how the arrows relate to the direction of events that occur
during this process.

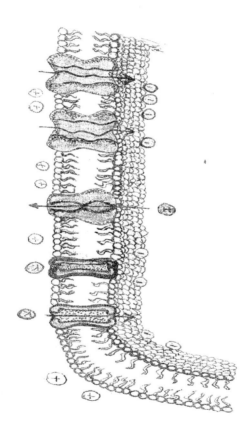

Chapter 11 Plant Growth

This chapter considers the following questions:
➢   What are the basic kinds of plant hormones and their functions?
➢   What are the basic processes and movements involved in plant growth?
➢   What are some of the varieties of plant responses to stimuli?

I. Plant Hormones and Growth
A. Plant Growth
1. Growth is an increase in the number of cells and involves mitosis in meristems.
2. In plants, growth may be determinate, meaning that plants grow to a certain size and then stop. Or indeterminate, in which growth continues throughout the life of the plant.
3. All plants begin as a single cell. As more cells are produced, they begin to differentiate into different plant tissues that specialize to perform specific functions. The differentiation process is called development. Development is controlled by hormones.

B. Plant Hormones
1. Growth and many other metabolic activities of plants are controlled directly by hormones.
2. Hormones are chemical substances, usually proteins and steroids, synthesized in one part of the plant and transported to another where they produce a specific effect.
3. Some hormones are activated or influenced by vitamins which are organic compounds produced only in plants that act as activators for enzymes.
4. Both hormones and vitamins are growth regulating substances.

C. Major Plant, Major Hormones
1. Auxins were the first plant hormones to be discovered.
2. Auxins function to promote growth in plants.
> (a) Auxins are produced in primary apical meristem.
> (b) Reactions of cells to auxins is determined by the concentration of auxin, the location of the cell and other factors. Same concentration of auxin that promotes shoot growth will inhibit root growth.
>> (1) Many monocots are less sensitive to auxins than dicots.
>> (2) Shoots are less sensitive to auxins than roots.
>> (3) Very high concentrations of auxins kill plant tissue.

3. There are three kinds of auxins.

> (1) IAA-(Indolacetic acid) stimulates formation of roots and organs. Some have been synthetically prepared and are widely used as rooting powder in nurseries.

>> ---IAA is sprayed on fruit trees to promote uniform flowering and fruit set.
>> ---IAA is also sprayed on fruit to prevent premature fruit drop, thereby allowing all fruit to be picked at one time.
>> ---IAA auxins applied to flowers before pollination results in seedless fruit.
>> --- IAA can also control number of fruits that mature.

> (2) PAA- (phenylacetic acid) is more abundant but less active than IAA.
> (3) 4-chloro IAA-(4-chloro-indoleacetic acid) germinates the seeds of legume plants such as mustards.
> (4) Synthetic Auxins-2,4-D; 2,4,5-T; 2,4,5-TP kill weeds and are widely used as herbicides.

>> ---Most synthetic auxins are harmless to humans but 2,4,5-T is banned in the U.S.
>> ---Agent Orange is a one-to-one mix of 2,4,5-T and 2,4-D.
>> ---It has been implicated in birth defects, leukemia, liver and lung disease, and miscarriages.

2. Gibberellins include 70 or more compounds isolated from seeds (especially dicots) or fungi, also occur in algae, mosses and ferns. Acetyl coenzyme A is a precursor of gibberellins.

> a. Gibberellins function to increase growth rates and are stronger than auxins alone. Auxins must also be present for gibberellins to act at maximum strength. Most dicots except conifers respond to gibberellins.
> b. Gibberellins increase stem length and emergence of flowers and seeds from dormancy. Can also stimulate plant growth at lower temperatures.
> c. Gibberellins stimulated lawn growth, causing it to turn green a few few weeks earlier in the spring. They are also important in producing seedless grapes and increasing the size of the fruit.

3. Cytokinins promote cell division. Several kinds of cytokinins are known. They occur in meristems and other developing tissues, especially young fruit. Cytokinins cause enlargement of cells, differentiation of tissues, development of chloroplasts, stimulation of cotyledons and delay in aging of leaves.

a. Cytokinins prolong life of vegetables in storage.

---Synthetic cytokinins are used to regulate the height of ornamental shrubs and keep harvested lettuce and mushrooms fresh.

---Cytokinnins shorten straw length in wheat so plants are shorter and don't blow over in wind.

---Cytokinins also lengthen the life of cut flowers.

4. Abscisic Acid- (ABA) is a hormone synthesized in plastids from carotenoid pigments.

a. ABA is common in plants and in fleshy fruits where it prevents seeds from germinating while still on the plant.

b. ABA usually inhibits growth. It is transported in xylem and phloem.

---When applied to plant buds the leaf primordial becomes bud scales and the bud becomes dormant.

---ABA is used to treat nursery plants that are shipped long distances.

---ABA effects can be reversed by application of gibberellins.

5. Ethylene is a gas hormone produced by fruits, flowers, seeds, leaves and roots. Some fungi and bacteria also produce ethylene either as a waste product or as a hormone.

a. Ethylene functions to induce flowering, ripening of fruit, speeds, release of seeds, and stimulates hypocotyls growth of seedlings up through the soil.

---A surge of ethylene occurs if the plant is cut or bruised.

---Ethylene is used commercially to artificially ripen harvested green fruits such as bananas and to color citrus fruits.

D. Interactions of Hormones

1. Apical Dominance is caused by an auxin-like inhibitor and results in the suppression of growth of axillary or lateral buds. This results in conical shapes of conifers such as pines. Apical dominance is weaker in deciduous trees such as ashes, elms, willows, that have much greater branching.

2. Senescence refers to the process of cell death. Leaf death and drop illustrates senescence. Hormonal control of senescence in plants is promoted by ABA and ethylene.

3. A combination of auxins, gibberellins, and cytokinins delay senescence.

E. Other Hormonal Interactions

1. Control of root and shoot growth is regulated by a combination of auxins and cytokinins. E.g., auxins cause living pith cells of tobacco plants to enlarge but mitosis does not occur unless cytokinins are present. Varying amounts of cytokinins can cause pith cells to differentiate into roots or buds from which stems can be produced.

II. Plant Movements
A. Growth Movements

1. Growth Movements result from varying growth rates in different parts of a plant organ. Growth movements are usually most pronounced in the young parts of plant. Stimuli for growth movements are internal or external.

B. Types of Growth Movements

1. Helical movements spiral around a common point and occur in many plants.
2. Nodding movements seen in legume family are a slow oscillating or side-to-side motion that facilitates progress of the growing plant tip up through soil.
3. Twining movements are stimulated both externally and internally. Stems of climbing plants elongate at different rates along their length. The twining movements of tendrils results from the elongation of cells on the side opposite the point of contact, causing the tendril to bend toward contact. Some tendrils coil due to auxins, others due to ethylene.
4. Contraction movements occur in roots of some plants, pulling the root into the ground.
5. Nastic movements help flatten plant organs such as leaves and flower petals.

III. Tropism-Caused Movements
A. Movement in response to external stimuli are called tropisms.

1. Phototropism is a basic plant growth response to direction of plant light.
   a. Most plant parts show positive phototropism, growing towards light source, e.g., twisting of stem of plant or petioles of leaves to enhance photosynthesis.
   b. Negative phototropism refers to movements away from light. Two examples include root growth away from light and twisting of leaves to avoid direct sunlight.
2. Gravitropism refers to growth in response to gravity. Primary roots of plants are positively gravitrophic. Cells detect gravity by movements of starch grains in cells in root cap called statoliths. Plant hormones such as auxins, and ABA may also be involved.

3. Thigmotropism is a growth movement in response to contacting a solid object, e.g., coiling of tendrils in climbing vines illustrates positive thigmotropism.

B. Turgor Movements

1. Sleep Movement occurs as leaves or flower petals fold at dusk and unfold at dawn. Cycles are called circadian rhythm and help to protect flowers. They are apparently controlled internally but can be altered by changing length of daylight. Movements are produced by turgor changes by passage of water in and out of cells at base of leaves and petals.
2. Contact Movements are sudden turgor changes caused by electrical charges released upon contact, or as a result of variation in light or temperature, e.g., Venus fly traps.

C. Photoperiodism.

1. Photoperiodism refers to influence of day length related to onset of flowering in plants.
2. Short-day plants don't flower unless photoperiod is shorter than critical length. Short day plants include asters, chrysanthemums, violets, goldenrods, ragweeds, and strawberries.
3. Long-day plants will not flower unless photoperiod is longer than critical period. Examples include beets, larkspurs, lettuce, potatoes, and wheat which usually, flower in summer.
4. Intermediate-day plants don't flower if days are too short or too long.
5. Day Neutral plants are primarily tropical plants that will flower at any photoperiod.

Multiple Choice Self-Test

_____ 1. The closing of a Venus flytrap is an example of: (a) a nerve firing (b) a muscle twitching (c) cell growth (d) cell migration.

_____ 2. Daily plant movements such as twisting of leaves is caused by: (a) cell growth (b) cell migration (c) turgor changes (d) temperature-caused dilations in leaves (e) all of the above.

_____ 3. The black walnut tree in your backyard prevents growth of other trees because: (a) its leaves shade out other trees (b) its roots suck up all of the soil nutrients (c) its roots such up all the soil water (d) its roots produce a chemical toxin that inhibits seedling germination.

_____ 4. Leaves and flower petals are flattened by means of: (a) giberillins (b) ABA (c) nastic movements (d) nodding movements.

_____ 5. Plant movement in response to touch: (a) gravitropism (b) thigmotropism (c) phototropism (d) all of the above.

Matching Self-Test

Match the hormone with its action:

_____ 1. Promote shoot growth	1. auxins
_____ 2. Promote apical dominance	2. ethylene
_____ 3. Increase growth rates	3. cytokinnins
_____ 4. Prolong storage life of vegetables	4. gibberellins
_____ 5. Inhibits growth	5. ABA
_____ 6. Increase stem length	6. Agent Orange
_____ 7. Promotes formation of roots	
_____ 8. Used in nurseries to regulate shrub height	
_____ 9. An effective herbicide	
_____ 10. Used in nurseries to induce flowering	

Concepts Self Test

1. Make a list of the basic nutrients that a plant needs for maintenance and growth and how and where they are obtained by the plant. Make a list of the chemical signals that stimulate plant growth and development.

2. Describe the components of movement that occur when a Venus flytrap closes.

3. Compare plants and animals with respect to the:
   (a) abscission in plants
   (b) plant dormancy
   (c) turgor responses to environmental stimuli
   (d) phototropism (responses to light)
   (e) dispersion in animals

4. What plant hormones do nurseries use to facilitate fruit production?

Test Your Association Skills

In the space below draw a rudimentary vascular plant, complete with flowers, stems, roots, and leaves. Label and describe the actions of the different plant hormones on the various parts of the plant that you have drawn.

Chapter 12 Meiosis and Life Cycles in Plants

This chapter considers the following questions:
➢   What is meiosis and how does it compare to mitosis?
➢   What are the steps in meiosis?
➢   What is alteration of generation in plants?
➢   What are the major types of alteration of generations in plants?

I. Introduction to Meiosis
A. General Concepts
1. Mitosis produces cells for growth and repair. During mitosis, the number of chromosomes in each new or daughter cell remains constant.
2. Plants like all other living organisms must reproduce to perpetuate the species. This reproduction can occur in asexual or sexual ways.
3. Vegetative spores are an asexual method of reproduction produced by mitosis.
4. Sexual reproduction is reproduction using seeds.
5. Seeds are produced by union of male and female gametes, which are eggs and sperm.
6. Union of sperm and eggs produces a single cell called a zygote.
7. Because chromosome number needs to remain constant, there must be reduction division in order to produce gametes. This reduction process is called meiosis. Meiosis is the process by which the chromosome number is reduced from diploid to haploid number.

II. Stages of Meiosis
A. General Information
1. As in mitosis, the chromosomes are double structures (chromatids) held together by the centromere. The goal of meiosis is to reduce this number of chromosomes by one half.
2. Meiosis goes through a series of stages and takes longer than mitosis. Mitosis is completed in about 24 hours, while meiosis may take up to two weeks to complete. The end result is the formation of haploid gametes, each with one complete set of chromosomes but half the number of chromosomes found in the diploid parent cell.

B. Events of Interphase
1. Interphase in meiosis is similar to interphase in mitosis. During interphase, the chromosomes are duplicated. Review interphase presented in the chapter on cells.

C. Reduction Division in Meiosis

1. Prophase I events include the coiling of chromosomes which become shorter and thicker and clearly showing two strands called the chromatids. Nuclear envelope disappears. Parts of homologous chromosomes may cross over. As in mitosis, some spindle fibers are attached to centromeres, whereas others extend from pole to pole.
2. Metaphase I is the second stage. In this stage, the chromosomes become aligned in pairs at the equator of the cell. At this time, the spindle is completed and becomes conspicuous. Metaphase I is like metaphase of mitosis except chromosomes at the equator are arranged so centromeres of homologous chromosomes are aligned opposite each other.
3. Anaphase I is the stage in which chromosomes migrate-one pair of chromosomes of each homologous pair migrates from equatorial plate to pole of cell.
4. Telophase I is the final stage of reduction meiosis. In this stage, the chromosomes usually enter directly into prophase II.

D. Meiosis Division II or Equatorial Division

1. Division II is similar to mitosis except that there is no initial duplication of the chromosomes as occurred to start Meiosis I. In Division II, each of the chromosomes (which usually consist of two chromatids held by the centromere) are split. That is, the centromere ruptures, and each chromatid now migrates to the opposite ends of the meiotically dividing cell. At the end of Meiosis II, the four resulting cells have a single set of chromosomes, i.e. are haploid. Thus, when an egg, which contains one set of chromosomes, unites with a sperm containing a second set of chromosomes (called fertilization) the new individual will have a complete set of chromosomes and is diploid or 2n.
2. Prophase II, is the stage in which chromosomes become shorter and thicker.
3. Metaphase II is the stage in which centromeres of chromosomes become aligned along the equator and a new spindle bundle forms.
4. Anaphase II begins when centromeres rupture and chromatids of each chromosome separate and migrate to opposite poles.
5. Telophase II is the final stage in equatorial division of meiosis. Chromosomes lengthens and become chromatin in the center of the cell. The nuclear envelope reforms and nucleoli organize for each group of chromosomes. As telophase II continues, the cell wall reforms, producing two new sex cells or gametes.

III. Alternation of Generations
A. General Information

1. Meiosis occurs in the sexual life cycle of plants.
2. The end product of meiosis is gametes, the egg and sperm.

3. Meiosis is a reduction in the chromosome number in the gametes.
   a. each gamete contains exactly half of the original chromosome number. That is, each gamete will end up with one complete set of chromosomes.
   b. This single set of chromosomes is termed the haploid number and symbolized as n.
   c. This differs from the original cell which contained two complete sets of chromosomes.
   d. A cell with two complete sets of chromosomes is called diploid. It is symbolized by 2n.
4. During meiosis, each diploid sex cell produces 4 haploid (n) cells.
   a. In most animals only haploid cells become gametes (sperm and egg).
   b. In plants this is generally not so. Rather, there is an alternation of generations between haploid and diploid plant generations.
5. The diploid generation is the spore producing sporophyte (2n) phase.
6. The haploid generation is the gametophyte (n) phase of life cycle.
7. Therefore, the diploid plant is the sporophyte and the haploid plant is the gametophyte.
8. To summarize, the typical life cycle of plants consists of an alternation of generations between a sporophyte generation and a gametophyte generation.

B. The Sporophyte Plant

1. The sporophyte generation is diploid. That is, each cell of the sporophyte plant contains two complete sets of chromosomes, the 2n or diploid number.
2. Sporophyte generation produces spores by meiosis. During meiosis, each reproducing cell in the sporophyte undergoes meiosis. This results in the production of four haploid (n) spores. Each of these four spores contains a single set of chromosomes.
3. The germination of each spore produces a multicellular gametophyte generation of plants. Each cell of this plant contains a single set (n) of chromosomes.

C. The Gametophyte Plant

1. The gametophyte generation is the sexually reproducing generation.
2. When gametophyte plants sexually reproduce, they form sex organs which mitotically produce male and female gametes (eggs and sperm). When these haploid gametes unite during fertilization, they produce a diploid sporophyte plant that is the sporophyte generation.
3. In the simple plants (also called the lower plants), the gametophyte phase of the life cycle is dominant.
4. In the higher plants (e.g., angiosperms) the sporophyte phase of the life life cycle is dominant.

D. Summary of Alternation of Generations in Plant Life Cycles

1. The first cell of the gametophyte generation is a haploid spore. The sexual cells are haploid gametes (the egg and sperm).
2. The first cell of the sporophyte generation is a diploid zygote and the last cell is an asexually produced haploid spore.
3. The change from the sporophyte to gametophyte generation occurs as a result of meiosis while the change from the gametophyte to a sporotophyte occurs as a result of fertilization.

Multiple Choice Self-Test

_____ 1. Cells with a single set of chromosomes are termed: (a) haploid (b) diploid (c) polyploidy (d) aneuploid (e) all are correct.

_____ 2. Pairs of chromosomes that line up in the middle of the cell at metaphase I are termed: (a) homologs (b) diplologs (c) chromatids (d) all of the above.

_____ 3. Which is part of the process of sexual reproduction? (a) spores (b) larvae (c) games (d) budding (e) fission (f) all of the above.

_____ 4. Cell plates that divide daughter cells appear in which phase of meiosis? (a) prophase I (b) prophase II (c) telophase II (d) all of the above.

_____ 5. The word alternation in the phrase "alternation of generation" means: (a) phase of a life cycle (b) phase of reproduction (c) change from one form to another form in a species life cycle (d) all of the above.

_____ 6. The sporophyte body of a plant develops from: (a) egg (b) spore (c) sperm (d) eggs and sperm (e) ovary (f) all of the above.

_____ 7. In asexual reproduction: (a) chromosome number is reduced from haploid to diploid (b) chromosome number is increased from diploid to haploid (c) chromosome number stays the same (d) polyploids are produced.

_____ 8. Fertilization results in the production of: (a) a haploid egg (b) a diploid zygote (c) a diploid sperm (d) all of the above (e) none of the above.

Matching Self-Test

_____ 1. Reproduction without sex		a. mitosis
_____ 2. Union of egg and sperm		b. meiosis
_____ 3. Generation that produces gametes		c. sporophyte
_____ 4. Generation that produces spores		d. gametophyte
_____ 5. Production of egg and sperm		e. fertilization
_____ 6. Body growth of sporophytes and gametophytes by?		f. asexual
_____ 7. Reproduction by eggs and sperm		g. sexual

Concepts Self-Test

1. What are the major similarities between mitosis and meiosis? How do they differ?

Chapter 13 Plant Genetics and Plant Breeding

This chapter considers the following questions:
➤   What is the science of heredity?
➤   What are the contributions of Gregor Mendel to the science of heredity?
➤   What are the basic laws and concepts of Mendelian genetics?

I. Introducing Genetics
A. General Information
1. Genetics is the study of genes, how they are transmitted from parent to offspring generations and how they are expressed in plants.
2. Heredity is another name for the science of genetics.
3. The science of heredity is important as plant breeding results in new forms of plants (called hybrids) food and material.

B. Gregor Mendel
1. Gregor Mendel was an Austrian monk who worked with peas. His work was overlooked until 1900, when other workers discovered laws of genetics independently and located his publications while they were searching through the scientific literature.
2. Mendel worked with pea plants which are self fertilizing or self-pollinated. This is important because the seeds of self-pollinated plants all have exactly the same genetic traits.
3. Mendel chose genetic characteristics that were easy to see and follow such as tall compared to short pea plants, smooth compared to wrinkled seeds and so forth.
4. Mendel began his studies by crossing tall plants with short plants. That is, he opened the flowers of tall pea plants, removed the anthers to prevent them from fertilizing themselves (self-pollination), then transferred their pollen to the flowers of dwarf pea plants. Thus, Mendel maintained strict scientific control of pollination in his crosses of pea plants. This ensured that his results would not be contaminated and confusing.
5. Mendel's pea plants produced all tall pea plants in the first generation.
6. Mendel allowed pea plants of the F_1 generation to self-pollinate to produce a second generation or F_2 generation. He found that this generation consisted of 3 tall and 1 dwarf pea plant.
7. Mendel continued to work with different crosses of pea plants, ultimately using results from his work to formulate the basic laws of genetics.

C. Mendel's Laws of Genetics
1. Each inherited trait is controlled by genes (Mendel called them factors).

2. Mendel called this law the law of unit factors.
   a. Genes control the expression of traits. For each trait, a pair of genes exerts the genetic controlling factors.
   b. If the genes are different at the molecular scale, they are called alleles. That is an allele is an alternate expression of a gene.
   c. For example, a pair of genes controls the genetic expression of the trait called height in pea plants. If the genes of the pair code for different aspects of the trait (one gene codes for tall, the other for dwarf), the two genes are said to be alleles of one another. An allele can therefore be defined as an alternate expression of a gene.
3. The Law of Dominance relates to dominant and recessive alleles in a gene set that codes for a single trait. In the example of pea plant height, the allele for tall pea plants is expressed whenever it occurs but the allele for dwarf pea plants is masked if the gene set includes an allele for tall. The allele for tall plants is therefore termed dominant and the allele for dwarf plants is termed recessive.
4. The Law of Independent Assortment refers to the fact that genes for different traits assort independently from one another when gametes are produced. Thus, in Mendel's studies, the genes that code for height assorted independently of the genes that coded for seeds.

II. Terminology of Genetics
A. Genes
1. The genes carried by a plant are called its genotype.
2. The appearance of the plant (tall compared to dwarf) is called the phenotype.
3. If both genes that code for a trait are the same (e.g., both tall) the genotype is termed homozygous.
4. If genes are different (1 tall, 1dwarf allele) the genotype is termed heterozygous.

B. Crosses
1. A monohybrid cross involves a single trait such as height in pea plants.
2. A dihybrid cross involves two traits, e.g., height and seed color in pea plants.
3. A backcross involves crossing the offspring with one of the true breeding parent plants to determine genotypes of the F_2 generation.

III. Modifications of Mendelian Genetics
A. Linkage or Linked Genes
1. Genes are located at specific points called loci on chromosomes. That is, a gene is a segment or section of DNA that provides the chemical code for a trait.
2. Genes located on the same chromosome are usually inherited together. That is, the plant inherits the chromosomes with its complement of genes.
3. This inheritance is called linkage.
4. Linkage differs from Mendel's Law of Independent Assortment because genes

carried on the same chromosome are inherited together.

5. Mendel did not observe this because the genes that he studied were carried on different chromosomes, hence were inherited (assorted) separately.

B. Crossing Over

1. Linked genes can be broken or intermixed by a process called crossing over.
2. Crossing over occurs during meiosis when homologous pairs line up at the metaphase plate.
3. In many species of plants, parts of the homologous chromosomes bend, twist, and intertwine with one another.
4. Sometimes these intertwined chromosomes fragment, then reform.
5. The reformed (or repaired) chromosomes contain a mix of alleles from each of the original chromosomes.
6. Crossing over is a kind of exchange process the two chromosomes lack one or more genes following the process. This is a source of mutations.

C. Incomplete Dominance

1. This genetic factor is an exception to Mendel's rule of dominance and recessiveness of genes.
2. Incomplete dominance occurs if neither allele is dominant, producing a "blend" of the trait.
3. An example of incomplete dominance is seen in 4 O'clock plants that produce either red or white flowers.
  a. If a red flower is crossed with a white flower, the F_1 flowers are all pink because neither allele is dominant, so both are equally expressed. The pink flower is actually a mix of red and white colors that we see as pink.
  b. If pink flowers are crossed, F_2 ratios are ¼ red, ½ pink and ¼ white.

D. Multiple Gene Inheritance

1. Some traits are coded by two or more sets of genes.
2. Seed color is produced as the result of several interacting gene sets.

E. Cytoplasmic Inheritance

1. Cytoplasmic inheritance refers to inheritance directed by genes located in the cytoplasm of cells.
2. Results from female contribution as male cytoplasm does not enter the 'egg."
3. Cytoplasmic inheritance typically involves the inheritance of genetic materials found in plastids and mitochondria, each of which have their own DNA.

IV. Changes in Genetic Structure
A. Mutations
   1. Mutations refer to a change in the molecular structure along a DNA molecule. Generally, a mutation occurs when one or more nitrogenous bases of a gene are changed. This is called a point mutation. If a mutation occurs the gene can no longer produce the trait.
   2. Mutations can be caused by exposure to physical and chemical conditions called mutagens.
   3. Most mutations are harmful (deleterious) and cause death of the plant if dominant. The mutations carried by a population are collectively called the genetic load.

B. Polyploidy
   1. Organisms normally have two sets of chromosomes (diploid), one set inherited from each parent. Thus, you inherit one set of chromosomes from your father and another set from your mother. For example, your 46 chromosomes are actually two sets of 23 chromosomes.
   2. Polyploidy is actually a type of mutation involving the inheritance of more than two sets of chromosomes. Polyploidy plants are often larger and more vigorous than diploids.

V. Plant Breeding
   1. Plant breeding is how modern crops are produced.
   2. Plant breeding is centuries old. Native peoples of much of the world used techniques of plant breeding to improve:
        a. size of plants.
        b. size of fruits.
        c. palatability of crops.
        d. resistance of crops to disease, pests, parasites.
   3. Horticulturalists use plant breeding to produce colorful varieties of the flowers, shrubs, and ornamental trees.
   4. Horticulturalists also use plant breeding to produce special strains or varieties that are adapted to different habitats
   5. Botanists today use plant breeding techniques to improve or provide:
        a. high yield crops
        b. drugs and other medicines
        c. paper products
        d. wood products
   6. Most plant breeding involves hybridization in which two varieties with favorable characteristics are crossed to produce a hybrid.
   7. When a high quality hybrid is produced it is inbred to reinforce that particular desired characteristic

VI. Plant Breeding and the Green Revolution

1. Global program initiated following World War II to produce high yield varieties of crops.
2. Extensive and intensive hybridization programs in Mexico, India, the Philippines produced valuable types of rice, wheat, and corn.
3. Green Revolution worked by:
   a. Increasing yields.
   b. Increasing the number of crops that could be produced each year.
   c. Increasing amino acid content of certain crops such as high lysine corn in Mexico.
   d. Increasing hardiness of certain varieties.
   e. Increasing disease resistance of certain varieties.

Basic Genetics Terms to Know

Allele. An alternate expression of a gene. A is an allele of a (and a is an allele of A) in the genotype Aa.

Genotype. The collection of genes carried by the organism.

Phenotype. Genes expressed in the appearance of the organism.

Dominant Gene. One that is always expressed in the phenotype.

Recessive Gene. One that is not expressed in the presence of a dominant gene

Homozygous. Alleles are the same, as in BB or CC.

Heterozygous. Alleles are alternate expressions as in Bb or Cc.

Incomplete Dominance. Also called codominance, neither allele is dominant, so both are expressed equally.

Multiple Choice Self-Test

_____ 1. Mendel derived the fundamental laws of genetics during his studies of:
(a) humans (b) pea plants (c) potatoes (d) all of the above.

_____ 2. The genetic development of new high yield varieties of rice and corn is called:
(a) Red Revolution (b) Green Revolution (c) Evolution (d) Hybridization.

_____ 3. The phenotype of an organism is the result of genes interacting with: (a) climate
(b) soil (c) animals (d) other plants (e) all of the above.

_____ 4. Transfer (loss) of a segment of a chromosome to another chromosome is termed:
(a) translocation (b) deletion (c) crossing over (d) all of the above.

_____ 5. The position of a gene along a chromosome is known as: (a) locus
(b) placement (c) tetrad (d) genotype (e) allele.

_____ 6. Genes that do not assort separately are termed: (a) alleles (b) deletions
(c) linked (d) dominant (e) recessive (f) gametes.

_____ 7. Another name for sex chromosomes: (a) gametes (b) alleles (c) linked
(d) all of the above (e) none of the above.

_____ 8. Changes in gene structure are collectively termed: (a) deletions (b) changes
(c) mutations (d) recessive (e) all of the above.

_____ 9. This results if pairs of chromosomes fail to separate during anaphase of meiosis:
(a) deletion (b) duplication (c) polyploidy (d) all of the above.

_____10. The phenotype is not always dependent completely on dominant alleles
because: (a) environmental influences (b) multiple genes (c) incomplete
dominance (d) epistasis (e) all of the above.

Matching Self-Test

_____ 1. Appearance of an organism

_____ 2. Genes carried by an organism

_____ 3. Multiple sets of genes

_____ 4. Two or more gene sets producing a result

_____ 5. Neither gene dominant

_____ 6. Alternate expression of a gene

_____ 7. Exchange of genes between homologous chromosomes

a. polyploidy

b. incomplete dominance

c. phenotype

d. genotype

e. multiple gene inheritance

f. crossing over

Genetics Problems: Do your work in the space provided

1. Red flowers in pea plants are produced by the allele R. White flowers are produced
by the allele r. Red is dominant and white is recessive. If you crossed white flowered
plants with white flowered plants how many different colors will occur in the progeny? If
you crossed red flowered plants with red flowered plants would you expect to get only
red flowered plants? Explain by means of simple Punnet Square examples.

Chapter *14* Plant Evolution

This chapter considers the following questions:
➢   What is evolution?
➢   What is the history of the development of the concepts of evolution?
➢   What were the contributions of Charles Darwin to Evolution?
➢   How does evolution work?
➢   What are the basic kinds of evolution?

I. Definition and Concepts of Evolution
A. General Information
   1. Evolutionary concepts derived from a need to classify organisms.
   2. Evolution is the long term genetic adaptation of a population to its environment. Evolution works to increase the fitness of the organism to its environment. The environment selects genetic traits that increase fitness.
   3. Ultimately, evolution is the process by which modern species of plants and animals are derived directly or indirectly from species of earlier times. These lines of descent stem originally from a simple unicellular ancestry.

B. The Genetics Basis of Evolution
   1. The environment determines the most adaptive phenotypes of a species population. That is, the members of a population live in an environment that includes other species populations. Those members of a population that are genetically best fit to exploit needed resources and adapt to environmental conditions survive and reproduce. The genes that make them more fit are passed to subsequent generations. Less fit members die.
   2. Note that evolution is the process in which the environment selects phenotypes that are the most fit phenotypes. Evolution does not directly select the genotypes that code for the phenotypes.

II. Development of the Concept of Evolution
A. The Predecessors of Charles Darwin
   1. Thoughts about how plants and animals evolve were first considered by the Greek scientist, Aristotle, who believed that organisms could be ranked from simple to complex.
   2. The religious dogma of the Middle Ages, rejected the idea about evolution, instead suggesting that each plant and animal species was specially created in preset form and was immutable.
   3. The geologist, Charles Lyell, was one of the first to determine that the earth was very old.

4. In 1780, the French scientist, Buffon, suggested that species are not permanent.

5. In 1800, Erasmus Darwin, grandfather of Charles Darwin, entertained ideas about how plants and animals may have evolved from their presumed ancestors over long geological time periods.

6. In the early 1800's, French scientist, Jean Baptiste Lamark, proposed that evolution occurred via the theory of **inheritance of acquired characteristics**. That is, the traits acquired in the lifetime of an organism were transmitted to succeeding generations. This is also called the theory of use and disuse, i.e., a giraffe gets long neck by stretching for leaves in trees. Its "stretched neck" is passed on to its offspring.

7. English naturalist, Charles Darwin, proposed the modern theory of evolution in 1859. As a student in 1828, Charles Darwin had traveled around the world on HMS Beagle, working as the naturalist for the expedition. During his travels, Darwin amassed a tremendous number of species and a large amount of data about flora and fauna of the world. He solidified his ideas about evolution in his monumental book, The Origin of Species.

8. Charles Darwin and another English naturalist, Alfred Russell Wallace outlined the ideas of evolution via natural selection.

III. Charles Darwin and Natural Selection
A. Principles of Natural Selection

1. Darwin noted that all species populations exhibit variation. That is, all individuals differ somewhat from one to another, e.g., height in humans.

2. Reproduction. With exception of endangered species, all normal populations of species reproduce far more individuals than can actually survive (can be supported by the environment). Yet, the size of all species population in natural environments remains fairly constant over time, given that the environment remains the same.

3. Therefore, there must be a constant struggle for existence between the members of a species population. That is, ecologically, all members of a species population are in constant competition with one another for resources.

4. Only the most fit members of a population can survive. By definition, the most fit members of a population are those individuals that can best exploit their environment, out competing other members to obtain the needed resources such as nutrients (food) and space. This tenant of natural selection is sometimes called survival of the fittest. The less fit members die and don't reproduce, so their less fit genes die with them.

5. The "fit" members of a population survive and reproduce, thereby passing the genes that make them so fit on to their offspring. Therefore, the offspring inherit the best genes.

6. Again, natural selection acts to select the phenotype which is produced by the genes. So, the phenotype rather than the genotype is actually selected during natural selection.

B. Types of Natural Selection

1. Stabilizing selection occurs when the environment is stable. In stabilizing selection, the members of the population that exhibit extreme variations are eliminated.
2. Directional selection occurs when environmental changes promote evolution in a specific direction. For example, as trees grew taller over a ecological time the giraffe species population that browsed in the tops of trees developed progressively longer necks---this resulted because the long necked giraffes were selected while short neck giraffes were not. That is, the long necked giraffes could obtain food, the short necked giraffes starved to death, ultimately producing a population of long necked individuals.
3. Destabilizing selection occurs when environmental changes results in different segments of a population evolving in different pathways, ultimately producing new species from a single species.

IV. Aspects of Evolution

A. Mechanisms of Evolution (how evolution works)

1. The science of genetics had not yet developed, so Charles Darwin could not explain the reasons for the variations that he observed in populations. Now we know that genes are the cause of these population variations.
2. Mutations result from changes in genes or chromosomes. Mutations provide the raw material for evolution to work on. Mutations can be the result of one or more changes in base pairing along the DNA segment of a gene. These are called point mutations. Point mutations change the chemical blueprints and may prevent the production of enzymes.
3. Mutations can also involve parts of chromosomes or entire chromosomes. Examples include deletions or duplications of all or part of a chromosome, translocation of genes along the length of a chromosome, inversions of parts of a chromosome, or polyploidy.
4. Perhaps, 99% of all mutations are deleterious or harmful to the organism. Only a small number of mutations actually increase the fitness of the individual.
5. Harmful mutations may be retained in a population as recessive genes for long time periods.

B. Factors Affecting Evolution

1. Genetic Drift occurs in small population in which genes may be lost from the population purely by chance.
2. Isolation. Geographic isolation results in the fragmenting of large populations into small populations. Isolation increases the chances for new species to develop.

C. Rates and Types of Evolution

1. Darwin and most modern biologists believe that evolutionary processes are slow and that natural selection acts over a long period of time.
2. In 1980, two American biologist, Niles Eldridge and Stephen J. Gould, proposed a theory of Punctuated Equilibrium, which is used to explain rapid shifts in evolutionary trends sometimes seen in the fossil record.
3. Evolution operates slowly most of the time, then under certain circumstances such as changing environmental conditions, evolution can occur rapidly.
4. Convergent evolution refers to evolution in which ancestors different but descendants are similar because of evolutionary adaptation for a similar way of life. Examples include bats and birds.
5. Parallel evolution refers to organisms that exhibit parallel development similarities because they share a common ancestor (humans and apes).

V. Evidence for Evolution

A. Evidence from Fossils

1. Fossils provide the single most powerful evidence for evolution of life on earth. The study of fossil life is called paleontology. Scientists that study paleontology are paleontologists.
2. Fossils are defined as remnants or traces of species that previously existed but are now extinct. Fossils include physical remnants of bodies or body parts or traces of former life. For example, a dinosaur fossil may include the preserved skeleton, bones, skin impressions, or even dinosaur footprints or tail drags across an old lake bed.
3. Most plant fossils are impressions but some plant parts can be petrified, meaning that their soft anatomy has been replaced, molecule by minerals. Or, they may be carbonized, in which case all the volatiles are boiled off by heat leaving behind a carbon impression. Coal is a good example of plant carbonization.
4. Sometimes, plant fossils are in the form of fossil pollen, which can be used to identify the presence of plant species in ancient communities or information about fossil climates.

B. Comparative Anatomy

1. Plant evolutionists can use homologies and analogies to determine evolutionary relationships.

D. Molecular Studies and DNA

1. Modern studies of plant DNA have shed much light on the evolutionary relationships of plants by comparing DNA sequences.

Table 14.1. Key Periods in the history of life on earth.

Millions of Years Ago	Era	Period	Epoch	Some Major Events in the History of Life on Earth
4600 3800 3500 2200 2000 1000	Precambrian			-origin of earth and solar system -origin of first living prokaryotic cells, the earliest bacteria -origin of photosynthesis -atmospheric oxygen content increases due to photosynthesis - Evolution of the first eukaryotes, the single-celled algae -First multicellular plants and animals evolve
544-505	Paleozoic	Cambrian		-Marine animals and marine algae common and widespread
505-440		Ordovician		-First fish, fungi appear
404-410		Silurian		-First vascular plants, land plants and animals appear
410- 360		Devonian		-Vascular plants spread over landscape, amphibians, insects
360-286		Carboniferous		-Club mosses and tree ferns form the great swamp forests.
286-245		Permian		-Insects and reptiles dominate land -Rise of gymnosperms.
245-208	Mesozoic	Triassic		-Gymnosperms forests dominate the land areas. First mammals and birds evolve.
208-146		Jurassic		-Dinosaurs dominate the world's land and sea habitats.
146-66		Cretaceous		-Angiosperms evolve and spread across earth, end of period marked by extinction of dinosaurs.
65-54	Cenozoic	Tertiary	Paleocene	-Flowering plants dominate as well as birds and mammals.
54-38			Eocene	-Flowering plants dominate

38-23			Oligocene	-Flowering plants dominate
23-5			Miocene	-Flowering plants dominate
5-2			Pliocene	-Flowering plants dominate
2-01		Quaternary	Pleistocene	-Evolution of humans
01-now			Recent	-Widespread human-predicated dispersal of plants across the global landscape

Multiple Choice Self-Test

_____ 1. North American forests during the Carboniferous period were dominated by: (a) ferns and flowering plants (b) ferns and gymnosperms (c) mosses and ferns (d) conifers and angiosperms (e) bryophytes and mosses.

_____ 2. Factor that contributes to evolution: (a) geographic isolation (b) mutations (c) genetic drift (d) all of the above (e) none of the above.

_____ 3. Evidence for evolution includes: (a) fossils (b) comparative anatomy (c) comparative morphology (d) protein structure (e) all of the above.

_____ 4. Early evolutionist who advocated the inheritance of acquired characters: (a) Lamarck (b) Wallace (c) Darwin (d) Dr. Avery (e) all of the above.

_____ 5. Which best applies to mutations? (a) always occur at a constant rate (b) may occur in sporadic rates (c) are mostly harmful or deleterious (d) all of the above (e) none of the above.

_____ 6. Plants that produce millions of spores or eggs or pollen illustrate: (a) survival of fittest (b) reproduction of fittest (c) overproduction (d) struggle for existence (e) inheritance of acquired characteristics.

_____ 7. Natural selection in which extremes are eliminated is termed: (a) directional (b) stabilizing (c) disruptive (d) all of the above.

Matching Self-Test

_____ 1. Epoch of evolution of humans
_____ 2. Era of Dinosaurs
_____ 3. Period of first land plants
_____ 4. Era of prokaryotes
_____ 5. Period of coal forests
_____ 6. Era of new life following dinosaur demise
_____ 7. Era in which flowering plants dominated
_____ 8. Period in which flowering plants evolved
_____ 9. Period of first vascular plants
_____ 10. Era in which photosynthesis evolved
_____ 11. Fungi first appeared in this period
_____ 12. Rise of gymnosperms in this period

a. Mesozoic
b. Pleistocene
c. Cenozoic
d. Paleozoic
e. Carboniferous
f. Cretaceous
g. Silurian
h. Precambrian
i. Ordovician
j. Permian

Matching Self-Test

_____ 1. Geologist that determined age of earth
_____ 2. Biologist that identified natural selection
_____ 3. Use and disuse theory proclaimed by this scientist
_____ 4. Charles Darwin's competitor
_____ 5. First to rank organisms from simple to complex

a. Charles Darwin
b. Wallace
c. Charles Lyell
d. Aristotle
e. Lamark

Concepts Self-Test

1. What is the relationship between evolution and genetics? Which discipline contributes what to which discipline. Does evolution contribute anything to genetics?

2. How can a study of the different groups of plants and other organisms, from bacteria to angiosperms, contribute to a theory of evolution?

Chapter 15 Plant Taxonomy

This chapter considers the following questions:
➢ What is the science taxonomy and what are its aims?
➢ What is the binomial system of nomenclature?
➢ How are the organisms of the world classified into kingdoms?

I. The Science of Taxonomy and Classification
A. General Information and Definitions:
1. Taxonomy is the science of identifying, naming, and classifying all of the living organisms of the world. Taxonomists also are involved in identifying and naming prehistoric organisms.
2. Scientists involved in taxonomy and classification are called taxonomists.
3. The goal of taxonomy and classification is to provide a systematic inventory of all of the living organisms of nature. This enables us to identify life and recognize their relationships.
4. Taxonomy and classification is based on similarities or differences in form, structure, morphology, chemistry, habitat, reproduction, development, and sometimes ecology.
5. Modern taxonomy and classification increasingly relies on DNA and RNA comparisons.

II. Linnaean Classification and the Binomial System of Nomenclature
A. History of Classification Attempts and Schemes
1. We talk about different kinds of plants. What we do mean by kinds? Basic unit of taxonomy is the species. The scientist must be able to do more than just recognize species. The scientist must classify and give names. This problem led to the development of taxonomy.
2. Aristotle proposed one of the first attempts at naming organisms. From his time until today, 375,000 kinds of plants and 1,250,000 million animals have been described. Each year, 5,000 more plants and 10,000 more animals are described, insects being the majority.
3. The use of common names, however, became confusing. A common and widely distributed plant such as broad leaf plantain, which occurs in Eurasia and the United States has hundreds of common names. 75 Dutch, 106 German, and 11 French for example.
4. The use of a single scientific name to designate the plant eliminates all confusion. The name applied to an organism is called the species name.

5. A species is then defined as a population of unique individuals that share reproductive and other traits. Individuals of a species are able to interbreed with one another but not with individuals of another species.

B. The System of Binomial Nomenclature.

1. First proposed and used by Carolus Linnaeus, an 18th century Swedish botanist and naturalist. Linnaeus published an account of all known species using binomial nomenclature in 1758, as the 10th edition of "Systemae Natura". His book, "Species Plantarum" which was published in 1753 is considered the initial work on plant classification.
2. Linnaeus listed the scientific name for all known species along with a limited description of their basic characteristics.
3. For each species, Linnaeus proposed a scientific name that consisted of two parts, the genus and the species. The species is named using Latin or Greek roots for words. Thus the human species is called *Homo sapiens*. Homo is the genus name and sapiens is the species name. Since the name consists of two parts, it is called binomial nomenclature (bi= 2, nomenclature=names).
4. The scientific name can also include the name of the scientist that first discovered and named the species as in Latinized or Greek roots. *Mentha spicata Linnaeus*-spearmint.
5. Modern taxonomy often includes the subspecies. This is called the Trinomial System of nomenclature. The subspecies is often used to indicate a geographic race.

C. The System of Hierarchical Classification

1. Taxonomically, all organisms are organized into a hierarchy of categories.
2. The categories include species, genus, family, order, class, division and kingdom. Note that botanists group classes into divisions but zoologists group classes into phyla.
3. The categories are related to one another in a hierarchy of similarity. That is, all similar species are grouped within the same genera, all similar genera are grouped within the same family, all similar families are grouped into orders, and so forth to kingdom.
4. Each level is separated by specific characteristics that apply only to organisms at that level.
5. Plants are grouped into categories by matching their morphological characteristics and if possible studying their evolutionary histories.
6. Principles of morphological comparisons.
    a. Homologies refers to plant organs that have a common ancestry and may or may not have common function. For example, the trunk of a pine and a maple.

b. Analogies refer to organs and other structures that have a different ancestry but have the same function, e.g., seed of a pine compared to the spore of a fern.

7. Plants sharing homologies are more closely related than those sharing analogies. Taxonomists may also use embryology, physiology, parasitology, and DNA relationships in determining taxonomic and phylogenetic relationships of organisms to one another.

8. The species is the smallest taxonomic group. Only one type of organism can have a species name. For example, of the millions of known organisms, only humans have the scientific name *Homo sapiens*.

9. Application of the taxonomic hierarchy to the classification of two organisms is illustrated:

Sugar Maple	Humans
Kingdom Plantae	Kingdom Animalia
Division Anthophyta	Phyla Chordota
Class Dicotyledonae	Class Mammalia
Order Floriferae	Order Primates
Family Acericeae	Family Hominidae
Genus *Acer*	Genus *Homo*
Species *saccharum* Marsh. Sugar Maple	Species *sapiens* Linnaeus. Human

III. Classification of the Kingdoms of Life
A. The Kingdom Concept

1. Initially, all organisms were classed into the plant or animal kingdom.

2. Since too many organisms did not readily fit into one or the other kingdom, the five kingdom concept was proposed by Cornell ecologist Robert H. Whittaker in 1959.

3. An alternate classification scheme that is also currently popular, recognizes three domains of life: Bacteria, Archaea and Eukarya. The Bacteria and Archaea are bacteria types though sufficiently distinct to warrant separate domain status. The Eukarya include all the eukaryotes such as fungi, protistans, plants, and animals.

B. Characteristics of the 5 Kingdoms of Life

1. Monera include the bacteria and prokaryotic algae.

2. The Protista are eukaryotic organisms. They include the algae and protozoa. Protistans are considered to be single-celled organisms although, there are many colonial species.

3. The Fungi, are eukaryotic organisms that include the slime molds, flagellate fungi and true fungi. The lichens are sometimes included in this group.

Fungi lack chlorophyll and the ability to produce food via photosynthesis. Instead, most fungi absorb food in solution.

4. The Plantae include all higher plants above the protistans including the bryophytes, ferns and their allies. Gymnosperms and angiosperms are all considered to be members of this kingdom. Almost all plantae are vascular plants, have chlorophyll and use photosynthesis.

5. All eukaryotic, multicellular animals are included in the Kingdom Animalia. Animals differ from plants in lacking chlorophyll and lacking the ability to produce food via photosynthesis. Most animals, are motile, have a nervous system and a digestive system.

Multiple Choice Self-Test

_____ 1. The genus name is always distinguished from the species name because it: (a) is capitalized (b) is in Latin (c) is in Italian (d) all of the above.

_____ 2. The study of the relationships between organisms is called: (a) science (b) microbiology (c) taxonomy (d) systematics (e) analogy

_____ 3. Homology is illustrated by: (a) plant leaf and fern leaf (b) plant leaf and algae blade (c) cactus spine and rose thorn (d) all of the above.

_____ 4. The highest taxonomic category below kingdom in botany is: (a) class (b) division (c) phylum (d) variety (e) hybrid

_____ 5. The species concept is: (a) fixed and immutable (b) changes as we develop new and better techniques (c) well defined (d) in a constant state of flux

_____ 6. System of giving each plant species a unique name is termed: (a) Latin (b) binomial nomenclature (c) trinomial nomenclature (d) hybridization

_____ 7. Which does not belong to the Eukarya? (a) Fungi (b) Protista (c) Animalia (d) Archaea (e) all of the above (f) none of the above.

_____ 8. Which is not the name of a domain? (a) Plantae (b) Archaea (c) Bacteria (d) Eukarya (e) all of the above (f) none of the above.

_____ 9. The first scientist to propose binominal nomenclature was: (a) Charles Darwin (b) Charles Lyell (c) Carolus Linnaeus (d) David Avery

Matching Self-Test

_____ 1. Flowering plants   a. Fungi
_____ 2. Mushrooms and yeasts   b. Protista
_____ 3. Humans   c. Animalia
_____ 4. Birds   d. Monera
_____ 5. Green algae and diatoms   e. Plantae
_____ 6. Truffles and toadstools
_____ 7. Snakes and lizards
_____ 8. Mosses and ferns

Chapter *16*   Plant Ecology

This chapter considers the following questions:
- What is the science of ecology?
- What are the characteristics of populations?
- What are the characteristics of communities?
- What are the characteristics of ecosystems?
- What are some of the basic ecological processes in nature?
- What are the major biomes of the world?

I. The Science of Ecology
A. General Information
1. Ecology is the study of the relationships of organisms to each other and to their environment. Ecology includes the study of individual organisms and their environment, called autecology; and the study of groups of organisms to their environment, called synecology.
2. Ecology is a relatively new science, originating in the late 1800's with the work of Ernst Haekel, who coined the name, ecology from the Greek, *ecos*= house, and *ology*= study of , so the term ecology refers to the study of the house of life, which encompasses all organisms.

II. Ecological Units: Populations, Communities, Ecosystems
A. Characteristics of Populations
1. Populations are comprised of individuals of the same species that interact with one another and with their environment. These interactions may include intraspecific (competition within the population) competition for food, shelter, territory or space and mates.
2. Technically, a population includes all members of a species population. In many cases, the population of individuals is actually subdivided into smaller and localized populations called subpopulations that interact only rarely if at all. The combination of all populations is termed a metapopulation.
3. Populations are defined by specific characteristics including density, fecundity etc.
4. Density refers to the number of individuals that comprise the population. Density is a basic but important characteristic. Density is a quantified measure, and refers to the number of individuals per unit of area, e.g., trees per acre is a measure of density. Because most plants grow as they age two other measures of a population include frequency, i.e., how widely the individuals are dispersed within the habitat, and biomass, also

called dominance, which is a measure of the collectively relative size or biomass that a species population contributes to a habitat.

5. Fecundity is the productivity of the population. This is generally measured in the production of seeds, germination rate, production of roots, shoots and other components that increase the size of the plant species population.

6. Mortality refers to the loss of members of biomass from the plant species population. It may refer to the subtraction of individuals, loss of seeds or other productive components, or the loss of biomass.

7. Age structure is a measure of the contribution of different age groups to the population. For example, tree populations may consist of seedlings, saplings, immature and mature individuals. Population age structure is important because the data provides information.

8. Growth rate refers to how fast or slow the plant species population is growing.

B. Characteristics of Plant Communities

1. Communities are ecologically defined as groups of species populations interacting with one another.

2. Examples of communities may include a woodland community or wetland community. The community itself would include all of the bacterial, protistan, fungal, plant and animal species populations that occur within the confines of the wetland community.

3. Interactions that occur at the community level include predator-prey interactions, host-parasite interaction, and interspecific competition for nutrients and space.

C. Characteristics of Ecosystems

1. Ecosystems are defined as groups of species populations interaction with one another and with their environment. Thus, an ecosystem is comprised of one or more communities.

2. Ecosystems include two basic components called the abiotic and biotic components.

3. The abiotic component of an ecosystem refers to physical and chemical factors which often define the type of ecosystem present. Climate conditions, especially temperature and moisture, soil conditions, topography are all aspects of the abiotic component.

4. The biotic component of an ecosystem includes all of the species populations that occur in that ecosystem.

D. Biomes

1. A biome is defined as a group of ecosystems that have a similar growth form and are limited in distribution by similar abiotic factors.

2. A grassland biome encompass all of the grassland ecosystems in a given region, e.g., short-grass grassland ecosystems, mid-grass grassland and tall grass grassland ecosystems are part of the grassland biome.

III. Ecological Processes
A. Energy Productivity and Flow
1. Energy production and flow refers to the biotic production of energy by producer organisms of ecosystems. Producers are mostly green plants and photosynthetic bacteria.
2. The producers of an ecosystem convert a portion of the energy of sunlight into the energy of the chemical bond to make sugars, or plant biomass. This is called primary productivity.
3. Primary productivity varies between ecosystems. Tropical rain forests and certain kinds of wetlands are the most productive ecosystems, deserts are the least productive.
4. Plants consume a portion of their primary productivity for maintenance, growth, and reproduction. The rest is called net primary productivity. All other species populations in an ecosystem are dependent on the energy of net primary productivity.

B. Nutrient Cycling
1. Nutrients for plants include water, minerals, organic substances, and a substrate in wich to grow.
2. Nutrients exist in finite amounts in ecosystems. They cycle from the abiotic part of the environment, are incorporated into organisms, then are returned with the death and decomposition of the organism.
3. Thus, nutrients, cycle rather than flow (as in energy).
4. The types of nutrient cycles are based on the primary reservoir of the nutrient.
> a. Sedimentary nutrient cycles refer to nutrients that have a reservoir in soils. Examples include the minerals such as calcium, iron, zinc.
> b. Gaseous nutrient cycles refer to nutrients that have a primary reservoir in the atmosphere, such as oxygen and carbon dioxide. n.

C. Ecological Succession
1. Ecological succession refers to the ability of natural communities and ecosystems to repair themselves following stress or perturbations that disrupt them.
2. Ecological succession is a natural, biotically driven process, meaning that organisms cause the repair of habitats rather than animals. Thus, any disrupted habitat will repair and replace itself over time if left alone.
3. Succession occurs in an orderly, predictable fashion, as one successional community follows another.

a. The sequence of ecological communities during succession is called a sere.
b. Each stage in a sere is called a seral stage.
c. Succession stops when the climax community is reached.
4. The climax community is defined as the stable, self-perpetuating ecological community.

Multiple Choice Self-Test

____ 1. Factors that increase nitrogen in soil: (a) lightning (b) volcanic activity (c) meteor strikes (d) organisms (e) all of the above.
____ 2. Most of the oxygen in the atmosphere is from: (a) byproduct of photosynthesis (b) decoupling of water (c) always there (d) imported by meteors.
____ 3. North American prairie is also this biome: (a) tundra (b) tropical rain forest (c) temperate rain forest (d) grassland (e) veldt (f) pampas.
____ 4. Ecological succession is caused by climate and? (a) biotic activity (b) weather (c) rainfall (d) amount of snowfall (e) all of the above.
____ 5. The stable community is called: (a) climax community (b) disclimax community (c) seral stage (d) sere (e) all of the above.
____ 6. Interactions of plants and the environment occur at which level: (a) individual (b) population (c) community (d) ecosystem (e) all of the above (f) none of the above.

Matching Self-Test

____ 1. Ecology of an individual   a. biome
____ 2. Group of individuals of the same species   b. biosphere
____ 3. All biomes considered together   c. population
____ 4. Interacting groups of populations   d. ecosystem
____ 5. Populations interacting with environment   e. community
____ 6. Large contiguous ecosystems   f. autecology

Concepts Self-Test

1. List and distinguish between biotic and abiotic components of habitats. What are the most important abiotic environmental components of habitats for plants?

Chapter 17 Kingdom Monera:
Viruses and Bacteria

This chapter considers the following questions:
➢ What are the monera?
➢ What are the characteristics of the Kingdom Monera?
➢ What are the major groups of bacteria?
➢ What are viruses and how are they related to other life?
➢ What is genetic engineering?

I. The Monera as a Kingdom
A. General Information

1. The monera include the bacteria and blue-green bacteria. The blue-green bacteria used to be called the blue-green algae but are more closely related to bacteria than algae.

2. The bacteria of the kingdom Monera are representatives of the oldest and simplest forms of life on earth. Between 1.8-3.6 billion years ago, monerans were the only form of life.

3. Viruses are traditionally included in the study of bacteria but although the two groups are relatively simple they are not closely related to one another.

4. All monera are extremely small microscopic organisms.

5. About 2500 species of bacteria are recognized. They occur in all environments. About 90% of species are harmless or useful to us but the other 10% cause disease.

6. Some of the most beautiful colors and specticles under the sea comes from bacteria. Flashlight fish produce light from luminescent bacteria. Many bacteria have symbiotic relationships with fish. Symbiosis means an association or relationship. In this case both members in the relationship are benefited. This is also called mutualism. The fish provide food and a place to live for the bacteria and the bacteria help the fish find food.

B. Characteristics of the Monera

1. All bacteria are prokaryotic and lack a clearly defined nucleus. The DNA consists of a single circular strand located in a specific region of the cytoplasm called a **nucleoid region**.

2. Monerans also have up to 30-40 small rings of DNA called **plasmids** in cytoplasm. Plasmids replicate separately from the nucleoid.

3. Compared to eukaryotes, the monerans are relatively simple in cellular structure and complexity; they lack membrane bound organelle such as golgi bodies, mitochondria, and plastids. Bacterial ribosomes are about half the size of eukaryotic ribosomes.

4. Some species may occur as gelatinous matrix or clumped in long, chain like filaments. But each cell is completely independent.
5. Monerans have a cell wall for protection. The cell wall is strengthened by **peptidoglycans** which are combinations of amino acids and sugars. In some bacteria, the cell wall is also reinforced by sticky secretions that form a protective **capsule** covering the cell wall.
6. Nutrition in the monera is mostly by direct absorption of food through cell wall but the more advanced forms are photosynthetic bacteria or chemosynthetic bacteria.
7. Reproduction in monera is predominately asexual by fission. Sexual reproduction is lacking but genetic recombination does occur in some monera by **pili**. A pili is a miniature tube that connects adjacent monera for transfer of DNA from one to another. Once in the recipient cell the newly acquired DNA becomes part of nucleoid. Different strains of bacteria are donors and recipients.
8. Bacteria may also acquire DNA by **transformation** in which a living cell picks up fragments of DNA released by dead cells and incorporates them into its own nucleoid. The new combination of genes are codes for new combinations of characteristics.

C. Classifying Bacteria
1. Bacteria average only two or three microns in diameter and up to 60 microns in length.
2. They occur in three forms or shapes: **cocci, bacilli**, and **spirilli.**
     a. Cocci are spherical or elliptical in shape.
     b. Bacilli are rod shaped or cylindrical.
     c. Spirilli are spiral or helical in shape.
3. All bacteria are further classified into two distinct groups called positive bacteria and negative bacteria by their Gram Stain, which is named after Danish scientist, Hans Christian Gram. Bacteria are washed with violet dye, red dye, and alcohol.
     a. Gram-positive bacteria stain violet and are susceptible to antibiotics.
     b. Gram-negative bacteria stain red and are more resistant to antibiotics.
4. Taxonomically, there are two distinct groups of bacteria in the Kingdom Monera, the Archaebacteria or ancient bacteria and the Eubacteria or true bacteria.

II. Subkingdom Archaebacteriophytinea
A. The Archaebacteria
1. The Archaebacteria are the earliest and also the most primitive bacteria known.
2. They differ from other bacteria in several distinct ways: cell walls lack muramic acid, cell membrane contain lipids, and the unique structure of

their RNA molecules which is more similar to eukaryotes than to other bacteria.

3. Three distinct groups of Archaebacteria are known today, the methane bacteria, salt bacteria, and sulpholobus bacteria.

B. The Methane Bacteria

1. This is the largest group of Archaebacteria. They are anaerobic bacteria that are found in swamps, ocean, hot springs, lake sediments, animal intestines, sewage treatment plants and other areas not open to air.

2. Methane bacteria form methane gas from CO_2 and hydrogen. Methane is also called swamp gas and forms a major part of the atmospheres of Jupiter, Saturn, Uranus and Neptune.

3. Methane produced by methane bacteria may be used as a vehicle fuel and methane producing bacteria will be extensively used for fuel production some time in the future. Methane is cheap to produce and can be made from manure or other waste products. Sludge that is left after production also makes an excellent fertilizer. Already used for fuel production in Italy, France and India. In U.S. methane is used to produce hydrogen in commercial preparation of ammonia.

C. The Salt Bacteria

1. The salt bacteria forms the red color of shallow salt evaporation ponds and playas found in the West.

2. Metabolism of salt bacteria enables them to thrive under conditions of extreme salinity---hence their name of salt bacteria.

3. Methane bacteria carry on simple photosynthesis using a red pigment called bacterial **rhodopsin**.

D. The Sulpholobus Bacteria

1. Occur in sulphur hot springs like those found in Yellowstone National Park.

2. Almost all forms of sulpholobus bacteria are able to thrive at very high temperatures from 80°C and an acidic pH around 2. One form, *Thermo plasma*, lacks a cell wall.

III. Subkingdom Eubacteriophytinea
A. Division Eubacteriophyta Class Eubacteria

1. The Eubacteria are the largest single group of bacteria and include the unpigmented bacteria, purple bacteria, and green sulphur bacteria. They are called the true bacteria.

2. The true bacteria have muramic acid in their cells.

3. They are mostly heterotrophic; most are **saprobes** that obtain food from non-living organic matter. Along with the fungi the true bacteria are important

agents of decay and recycling of all types of organic matter. About 10% cause disease.

B. The Autotrophic Bacteria

1. Some species of true bacteria carry on photosynthesis without producing oxygen, using a greenish chlorophyll-like material called **bacteriochlorophyll**.
2. Some species are **chemoautotrophic**, obtaining energy by oxidizing inorganic substances and deriving energy from the process. For example, the process works like this: $CO_2 + 2H_2S \rightarrow Ch_2O + H_2O + 2S + energy$.
3. Economically, many of the true bacteria are important agents for composting. Composting bacteria take organic waste material such as garbage, manure, and leaves and convert it into compost, important for agriculture.
4. Bacteria also play a major role in the dairy industry as active working ingredients in culturing buttermilk, yogurt, sour cream, and cheese.
5. Lactic acid from bacteria induced processes is used in textile manufacture.
6. Other uses include as laundry products, as a leather agent, and in treating calcium and iron deficiencies.

C. True Bacteria and Disease

1. About 10% of true bacteria cause diseases of other organisms. Bacterial diseases of plants costs millions of dollars each year in lost crop yields for humans and farm animals. True bacteria also cause spoilage and decay.
2. Disease causing bacteria enter plants and animals through the air, in food, and in the water. The last is of special concern for humans.
3. **Access from the air** occurs from coughing, sneezing, or speaking loudly which produces invisible spray of saliva containing bacteria along with other microorganisms such as viruses. The fluid quickly evaporates but bacteria cling to protein flakes that enters human respiratory tracts. Examples include whooping cough, meningitis, pneumonia, and strep throat.
4. **Access Through contamination of food and drink** occurs from open sewers and other unsanitary conditions in some areas. Diseases include cholera, dysentery, staphylococcus and Salmonella food poisoning. Legionnaire disease results from contaminated water in air conditioning systems. Botulinum poisoning is caused by toxins produced by soil bacteria called *Clostridium botulinum* which can contaminate food and drink. Because *Clostridium botulinum* can survive and reproduce anaerobically, it sometimes occurs in food that has not been properly canned or cooked.
5. **Access Through Direct Contact** occurs in such sexually transmitted diseases as syphilis and gonorrhea. Anthrax and brucellosis bacteria enter the body through skin or mucous membranes. Anthrax is a disease of cattle and other farm animals that can be transmitted to workers in hide and wool industry.

6. **Access Through Wounds** occurs in tetanus (lockjaw) bacteria which are common soil bacteria that produce extremely dangerous toxins.
7. **Access Through bites of insects and other organisms** explains how bacterial diseases such as bubonic plague (black death), typhus, cholera, and tularemia are transmitted by fleas, ticks, or lice.
8. **Koch's Postulates** regarding bacterial diseases were formulated by the German physician Robert Koch, who investigated anthrax and tuberculosis in the late 1890s. Koch formulated four specific rules regarding the bacterial causes of diseases.
    a. Microorganisms must be present in all cases of the disease.
    b. Microorganisms must be isolated from victim in pure culture.
    c. When microorganism from a pure culture is injected into a susceptible host it must produce the disease in new host.
    d. Bacteria must be isolated from the experimentally infected host and grown in pure culture for comparison with that of original culture of disease causing bacteria.

IV. The Blue-Green Bacteria
A. General Information
1. The blue-green bacteria are a form of eubacteria. They were formally called blue-green algae. They differ from true algae in being prokaryotic, as in other bacteria.
2. Most blue-green bacteria have **chlorophyll a** which is also found in green plants. Oxygen is produced as a product of photosynthesis. The blue-green bacteria have blue phycocyanin and red phycoerythrin pigments.
3. Blue green bacteria are the only organisms that can fix nitrogen and produce oxygen.
4. Blue-green bacteria occur in diverse habitats. They are common in temporary pools and ditches and abundant in fresh water. They also occur in hot springs where they deposit calcium carbonate in the form of travertine. They invade and colonize new volcanic lava.
5. Their habitats range from tiny fissures in desert rocks to jungle soils, even on the shells of turtles and snails. Some live as symbionts with amoebae, other protozoans, diatoms, sea anemones, fungi and roots of tropical cycads. Some species team with fungi to form lichens.

B. Characteristics
1. Blue-green bacteria often occur in chains or hair like filaments. Some form irregular, spherical, plate-like colonies held together by gelatinous sheaths which may be colorless or pigmented with shades of yellow, red, brown, green, blue, violet or blue-black.
2. Cells are colored blue-green due to the presence of chlorophyll and phycocyanin pigments which produce the particular color.

3. They produce nitrogenous food reserve called cyanophycin. Also produce and store carbohydrates and lipids.

4. Blue-green bacteria lack flagella but some rotate in a gliding motion like *Oscillatoria*.

5. Reproduction is via fission or **fragmentation** of chains.

    a. In *Nostoc* and *Anabaena* which form chains, fragmentation occurs in cells called **heterocysts** which are also sites of nitrogen fixation.

    b. These two genera may also produce thick-cell walled cells called **akinetes** which resist freezing and other adverse conditions.

    c. Some can lie dormant for up to 80 years.

    d. Meiosis does not occur but some exhibit genetic recombination.

6. Blue-green bacteria are thought to be responsible for the addition of oxygen to the modern atmosphere. Beginning about 3.0 billion years ago, blue-green bacteria began to release oxygen into the atmosphere. By 1 billion years ago the amount of atmospheric oxygen sufficient to support plants and animals. By 500 million years ago enough ozone had accumulated to offer a protective blanket from solar ultraviolet radiation.

7. Ecologically, the blue-green bacteria are important photosynthetic organisms that form the base of many food chains, especially in aquatic habitats. They are also essential for their role in nitrogen fixation.

    a. Over 40 species of blue-green bacteria are able to fix atmospheric nitrogen and incorporate it into organic tissue.

    b. During summer, blue-green bacteria may form floating mats called pond scum which impart a bad smell and taste to water along with toxic substances that are often poisonous to livestock and other animals.

8. Economically, the blue-green bacteria clog filters, corrode steel and concrete, cause softening of water and produce odors and discoloration to water.

V. The Viruses
A. General Information

1. Viruses are important agents of many human diseases. Such as smallpox, rabies, measles, mumps and AIDS. Viruses are host-specific but most forms of life are susceptible to viral infections. The economical loss of life caused by viruses is enormous.

2. Viruses are smaller than bacteria and very simple.

3. Typical viruses are about the size of large chemical molecules and have a diameter of 15-300 nanometers.

4. Viruses are nonliving entities that consist only of simple strands of RNA or DNA strands, never both.

5. The genetic material is surrounded by a protein jacket for protection that may resemble a geodesic dome with a head and tail region in some.

6. Viruses "live" and reproduce only inside prokaryotic or eukaryotic cells

7. Characteristics of viruses include
   (1) complete lack of cellular structure.
   (2) do not grow by increasing in size or dividing.
   (3) do not respond to external stimuli.
   (4) cannot move on their own.
   (5) unable to carry on independent metabolism.
8. Viruses are very common-a teaspoon of seawater may contain 1 billion viruses.

B. Viruses and Diseases
1. **Bacteriophages** are viruses that attack bacteria.
2. In plants, most viruses are transmitted from plant to plant by insects such as aphids, produce dead patches of tissue on leaves or stems called **necrosis**. Most plant viruses have an RNA rather than DNA strand.
3. Many forms of cancer may be caused by viruses. Cells invaded by viruses produce interferon which interferes with further viral reproduction within the cell. AIDS is a viral disease.

Multiple Choice Self-Test

_____ 1. The rules that describe bacterial-disease relationships were first determined by: (a) Robert Koch (b) Louis Pasteur (c) Edward Jenner (d) Aristotle.

_____ 2. The circular DNA ring of bacteria is called: (a) nucleoid (b) thylakoid (c) desmosome (d) chloroplast (e) chromosome (f) gene.

_____ 3. A pathogenic bacteria: (a) absorbs dead plants and animals (b) absorbs live plants and animals (c) cause disease in plants and animals (d) all of the above (e) none of the above.

_____ 4. Factor important in the success of bacteria: (a) cell wall protection (b) cell wall and nucleoid organization (c) small size and activity (d) rapid reproduction rate (e) all of the above (f) none of the above.

_____ 5. Unlike photosynthesis in plants, photosynthesis in bacteria: (a) produces lipids (b) does not produce oxygen (c) does produce oxygen (d) all of the above.

_____ 6. An obligate anaerobic bacteria: (a) does not require oxygen to survive (b) does require oxygen to survive (c) produces its own oxygen to survive.

_____ 7. Where does photosynthesis occur in photosynthetic bacteria: (a) cell wall (b) nucleoid (c) chloroplasts (d) cell membranes (e) all of the above.

_____ 8. Bacteria cause disease via: (a) production of toxins (b) destruction of host cells (c) disrupting host cell metabolic function (d) all of the above.

_____ 9. The relationship between bacteria in human intestines is termed: (a) antagonistic (b) symbiotic (c) counterproductive (d) all of the above.

_____ 10. Bacteria are gram-stained to determine: (a) cholesterol levels (b) chitin levels (c) lipoprotein and lipopolysaccharide levels (d) glucose levels.

_____ 11. These bits of DNA are found in bacterial cytoplasm: (a) plasmids (b) nucleoids (c) capsules (d) pili (e) cocci (f) bacilli.

Matching Self-Test

_____ 1. Pioneer in vaccinations
_____ 2. Pioneer in establishing bacteria-disease rules
_____ 3. Circular or cylindrical bacterial form
_____ 4. Pioneer in gram staining of bacteria
_____ 5. Bacteria of swamps and hot springs
_____ 6. Photosynthesis via rhodopsin
_____ 7. Sulfur hot springs of Yellowstone
_____ 8. Nitrogen fixing bacteria

a. Sulfur Bacteria
b. Salt Bacteria
c. Robert Koch
d. Hans Gram
e. Bluegreen Bacteria
f. Louis Pasteur
g. Jenner
h. Hans Gram

Concepts Self-Test

1. Viruses are considered by most to be nonliving. A few biologists suggest that viruses are actually highly specialized living forms that spend most of their life cycle in a dormant state. Marshall evidence to defend both contrasting concepts.

2. Use the internet as a resource and discuss the importance of viruses in modern medical techniques, especially for the synthesis of drugs and other medicines.

Visual Self-Test

Label the generic example of a virus.

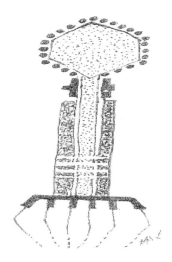

Visual Self-Test

Label the diagram of a representative blue-green bacteria below. Can you identify the akinetes and heterocysts? What is the significance of these structures relative to the reproduction of this species?

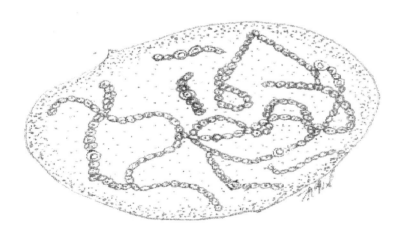

Chapter 18 Kingdom Protista: The Algae

This chapter considers the following questions:
➤ Are protistans and algae the same thing?
➤ What are the characteristics of the algae?
➤ What are the major groups of algae?
➤ What are some characteristic representatives of the major groups of algae?
➤ What is the economic importance of the algae?

I. Introduction to the Algae
A. General Information
1. The protistans include the animal protozoans and the plant called algae.
2. Some species such as *Volvox* and *Euglena* have intermediate characteristics and are studied in both zoology and botany courses.

B. Characteristics of the Kingdom Protista
1. All protistans are eukaryotic.
2. Many protistans are single-celled organisms but there are a number of colonial species.
3. Nutrition varies considerably within the kingdom. Algae are photosynthetic (autotrophic) and protozoans are heterotrophic. Some protistans are both autotrophic and heterotrophic.
4. Great variation in life cycles; both asexual and sexual reproduction occurs in many species.
5. Algae variable in shape and size but all lack true leaves, vascular system, or flowers.

II. The Division Chrysophyta-the Golden Brown Algae.
A. General Information
1. This division includes about 6,000 species, all microscopic. They are not well known, but all are beautiful for form and shape. There are four classes of golden brown algae.
2. All share same food reserves, specialized pigments and other cell characteristics in common. Some members in each class produce a resting cell stage called a statospore, which resembles a miniature bottle.
3. Taxonomically, the golden-brown algae consist of three classes:
   a. Class Xanthophyceae which are the yellow green algae.
   b. Class Chrysophyceae which are the golden brown algae.
   c. Class Bacillariophyceae which are the diatoms.

B. Diatoms

1. The diatoms are the most important economically of the division.
2. They are unicellular algae of both fresh and salt water that often occur in huge numbers, mostly in the colder marine climates of the world. Diatoms often occur as floral of damp cliffs, bark of trees, bare soil or sides of buildings.
3. There are more than 5,600 known species of diatoms.
4. Structurally, diatoms look like miniature glass pillboxes with one half of a rigid wall fitting over the other half. Most marine diatoms are circular but freshwater forms are fusiform.
5. Diatom walls contain 95% silica deposited on an organic framework of pectin.
6. Each diatom cell has one, two, or many chloroplasts with chlorophyll a, chlorophyll c1 and chlorophyll c2. Chloroplasts are golden-brown in color because of presence of a brownish pigment called **fucoxanthin**.
7. Eventually, each protoplast undergoes meiosis, producing 4 gametes which unite to form zygotes called **auxospores**. These rapidly increase in size then form cell walls.
8. Commercially, diatoms rank among the most important of all algae. **Diatomaceous earth** results when diatoms die and their bodies collect as ooze on the ocean floor to form a mush several hundred meters thick. This diatomaceous earth is commercially harvested and used in many filtration processes. It is also an ingredient in silver and metal polish, toothpaste, light reflecting paint, insulation around blast furnaces and boilers.

III. Division Pyrrophyta- the Dinoflagellates
A. Introducing the Dinoflagellates

1. Structurally, a dinoflagellate consists of external plates formed from cellulose just under plasma membrane of cells. The 2 flagellate are attached near each other in adjacent intersecting grooves. One flagella acts as a rudder trailing behind the cell, the other flagella gives spinning motion to cell.
2. Internally, a dinoflagellate has 2 or more disc-shaped chloroplasts that contain chlorophyll A and chlorophyll C along with brown pigments. Nearly 45% of dino-flagellates lack the ability to photosynthesize-instead they feed like animals and ingest food particles.
3. Photosynthetic dinoflagellates have an eyespot for orientation to light source.
4. All dinoflagellates have a unique nucleus in which the chromosome remain condensed and clearly visible throughout life of the cell. The chromosomes are also unique because they contain up to 40% more DNA than found in human cells.
5. Dinoflagellates are mostly algae of fresh and salt water habitats. Some are luminescent. Red tides occur when dinoflagellate populations rapidly increase, coloring the water red and producing a strong toxin that kills fish and shellfish, paralyze humans.

6. Reproduction is mostly by asexual binary fission or cell division. Sexual reproduction is rare.

IV. Division Euglenophyta- the Euglenoids
A. General Information

1. There are about 750 species of euglenoids. All are aquatic species which commonly occur in small ponds, pools, and other areas of still water.
2. *Euglena* is unique in that it can feed and function like an animal or photosythetically produce food like a plant. Therefore, Euglena is studied in both zoology and botany courses.
3. *Euglena* is a typical species consisting of a spindle-shaped cell surrounded by membrane reinforced with parallel spiral strips just under the membrane called a **pellicle**.
4. *Euglena* has a single flagellum that has numerous tiny hairs on one side which help "pull" Euglena through the water. A second, very short, flagellum is located within a **reservoir** at base of large flagellum.
5. Euglena has a **gullet** or groove for food ingestion when feeding as a **heterotroph**.
6. Most euglenoids also have **chloroplasts** and a **red eyespot** and store photo synthetically produced sugars in the form of **paramylon** bodies scattered throughout the cytoplasm.
7. Reproduction is primarily by asexual binary fission that occurs along the length of a euglenoid (longitudinal fission).

V. Division Chlorophyta-The Green Algae
A. Characteristics

1. Green algae are the largest group of algae, numbering about 7500 species.
2. Some species are unicellular, others form either plate-like, thread-like, or net-like hollow balls consisting of hundreds or thousands of cells. Some are in the form of seaweeds.
3. Green algae occur as growths of green patches on tree bark, in animal hair or skin, in sponges, flatworms, on backs of turtles, even in snow banks. The greatest variety of green algae occur in freshwater ponds, lakes and streams.
4. Green algae are an important part of oceanic plankton.
5. Cells of green algae have chlorophyll a and b, as found in like higher plants. They may be ancestral to green land plants.
6. Green algae store food in chloroplasts in form of starch (as in land plants). Most undergo both sexual and asexual reproduction.

B. The Green Algae *Chlamydomonas*

1. *Chlamydomonas* is common in quiet freshwater pools.

2. *Chlamydomonas* is an oval, unicellular cell that has a cellulose wall, a pair of whip-like flagella, and two vacuoles located near the base of the flagella. They regulate the water content of the cell.

3. *Chlamydomonas* has a single, huge cup shaped chloroplasts which partially obscures nucleus. The chloroplasts contains two **pyrenoids** that synthesize light.

4. *Chlamydomonas* reproduces sexually or asexually. During asexual reproduction, the flagella degenerate and drop off, nucleus divides by mitosis, and the protoplasm separates into daughter cells enclosed within the cell wall. Each daughter cell then develops flagella, escapes and swims away. Asexual reproduction (without sex) may occur repeatedly within a dividing cell resulting in up to 32 new daughter cells before wall ruptures.

5. During sexual reproduction, many cells congregate. Pairs of cells are attracted to each other by flagella and function as gametes. The cell walls of cell pairs disintegrates so the cytoplasm and nucleus combines into a single zygote which may remain dormant for many months. After emerging from dormancy, the diploid cell undergoes meiosis producing 4 haploid **zoospores** which swim away and become adult haploid algae.

C. The Green Algae *Ulothrix*

1. *Ulothrix* is a thread like algae consisting of a single row of cylindrical cells. At one end there is a slightly larger basal cell that functions as a **holdfast**.

2. *Ulothrix* is found on dead twigs, rocks and debris in cold water ponds, lakes, and streams.

3. The nucleus of *Ulothrix* is surrounded by a wide chloroplast shaped like a bracelet. Each chloroplasts has one or more **pyrenoids**.

4. During **asexual reproduction** in *Ulothrix* the protoplasts of a dividing cell clumps and condenses, then mitotically divides to produce **zoospores** with contractile vacuoles, eyespots and 4 flagella instead of two flagella seen in normal Ulothrix cells.

5. Each zoospore escapes via a pore through the cell wall, then swims about until it attaches to a suitable substrate such as a submerged object. Once attached the zoospore discards the flagella and begins to grow. One of the first cells produced becomes the holdfast for attachment to the substrate.

6. An alternate method of asexual reproduction occurs when some protoplasts divide but don't form flagella. Instead they are released when the cell wall ruptures and new filaments called **alanospores** are formed

7. During sexual reproduction, a protoplast divides, producing up to 64 zoospore-like cells, each with two flagella. Each zoospore functions as a gamete; pairs of zoospores unite to form zygotes. Zygotes may form thick walls and become dormant for a time, eventually the zygote undergoes meiosis

giving rise to new filaments. This kind of sexual reproduction involving identical-sized gametes is called **isogamy**.

D. The Green Algae *Spirogyra*

1. *Spirogyra* is a slender, filamentous green algae commonly called water silk. It is a common fresh water algae floating in mats in quiet water of streams and along edges of ponds.
2. *Spirogyra* has a unique, ribbon-like chloroplasts, with evenly spaced pyrenoids occurring at regular intervals along them.
3. Asexual reproduction is primarily by fragmentation, each fragment becomes a new individual, given the right habitat and climate conditions.
4. Sexual reproduction in *Spirogyra* is called conjugation.
    a. During conjugation, individual cells of adjacent filaments form dome-shaped papillae which grow together and fuse to form **conjugation tubes**.
    b. Condensed protoplasts function as gametes. Since both are the same size they are called isogametes.
    c. The mobile protoplast is considered to be the male and the the stationary protoplast is the female.
    d. The male protoplasts fuses with the female protoplast to form a zygote, which develops a thick, protective wall and remains dormant through winter.
    e. In spring, the wall is enzymatically dissolved, and meiosis takes place, resulting in 4 haploid cells.
    f. Three of the 4 cells disintegrate but the forth grows as a new filamentous *Spirogyra* organism.

E. The Green Algae *Oedogonium*

1. *Odegonium* is a filamentous green algae often found growing on a variety of aquatic plants including other algae as an **epiphyte** (an epiphyte is a plant that grows on the surface of another plant; epi = on top of, phyte = plant).
2. Structurally, *Odegonium* consists of a thread like series of cylindrical cells. Modified basal cells at one end are holdfasts that anchor the algae. Each cell contains a large net like chloroplast for photosynthesis along with pyrenoid bodies for starch storage.
3. Asexual reproduction may result in thick walled cells called **akinetes** that provide the over wintering stage. More commonly, cells at tips of filaments produce zoospores equipped with flagella. These fragments are released, swim about, then attach to a suitable substrate.
4. Sexual reproduction occurs in box-like cells called **anteridia** which form in the filaments adjacent to nonsexual (vegetative) cells.
    a. Each anteridia produces a pair of gametes that are termed **sperm**.

b. Other cells become round and swollen and are called **oogonia** because they produce eggs.

c. Sperm enter the oogonia via a small pore and unite with an egg to form a zygote.

d. The zygote undergoes meiosis to produce 4 zoospores each of which is capable of developing into a new filament.

e. This kind of sexual reproduction in which one gamete is larger and stationary than the other is called **oogamy**.

F. Other Green Algae

1. There are many varieties, shapes and life cycles of other species of green algae.

2. *Chlorella* is a common and useful research species. Future spaceships may carry tanks of *Chlorella* as useful for producing oxygen and food for the spaceship crew.

3. *Volvox* is a colonial green algae consisting of several hundred to several thousands cells held together in a secretion of gelatinous material and by cytoplasmic strands. The colony moves in a rolling fashion by means of flagella. Reproduction is sexual or asexual. Daughter colonies formed inside colony and released when parent colony breaks up.

4. *Ulva*, also called sea lettuce, is a colonial seaweed with large flattened green blades that may reach 1 meter in length. Blades of an individual *Ulva* are either haploid or diploid and anchored to rocks by means of holdfast. Diploid blades produce spores that develop into haploid blades bearing gametangia. Gametes from haploid blades fuse in pairs, forming zygotes and grow into the diploid adult *Ulva*.

VI. Division Phaeophyta-the Brown Algae
A. Introduction and Characteristics

1. Over 1500-2000 species of brown algae are brown to olive in color.

2. Brown algae are typically larger marine algae of cold ocean waters. Only four species occur in fresh water habitats. The giant kelp is one of the most familiar of the brown algae, occurring in water up to 30 meters deep. Long considered to be one of the largest of all living organisms, a giant kelp can measure over 200 meters in length (over 700 feet).

3. Structurally, the long body is anchored to the sea floor substrate by means of a **holdfast.** Most of the kelp consists of a long, leaf-like blade held by a stalk. Some kelp have gas filled **bladders** that help the blade float in the water.

4. Photosynthetic pigments include chlorophyll a and chlorophyll c along with fucoxanthin. Food is stored as a starch called **laminarin.**

5. Sargasso Sea is named for the brown algae *Sargassum*.

6. Reproduction is either sexual or asexual. Most brown algae asexually reproduce by fragmentation but some produce aplanospores.

7. Sexual reproduction in the brown algae is exemplified by *Fucus* which is a common rockweed.
   a. Reproductive cells have two flagella and are the only motile cells in this algae.
   b. Reproductive cells are formed in separate male and female **thali** which grow on *Fucus*.
   c. The tips of each thallus have puffy swellings called **receptacles**, within which are chambers called **conceptacles** containing **gametangia** (the gametes).
   d. Eight eggs are produced in each female gametangia (also called the oogonium) as result of a single diploid nucleus that undergoes meiosis.
   e. Male gamentangia (the anteridium) undergo meiosis followed by three mitotic division, producing a total of 64 sperm.
   f. Both eggs and sperm are released into water to eventually fuse and produce zygotes

8. Many brown algae are commercially very important. **Algin** from kelp and other brown algae helps control water content in foods and is used in the preparation of ice cream, salad dressing, beer, jelly beans, latex paint, penicillin suspension, paper, textiles, toothpaste, ceramics and floor polish. It also acts to stabilize suspension such as milkshakes.
9. Brown algae is harvested as livestock feed, as food for humans, and as an important source of minerals such as iodine, nitrogen, potassium, and substances such as acetic acid. It can be harvested and applied as a cheap fertilizer for crops.

VII. Division Rhodophyta- the Red Algae
A. Introduction and Characteristics

1. The red algae number some 5,000 species of red algae seaweeds that tend to occur in warmer and deeper waters than brown algae. Many species are also found on rocks of intertidal zones where they are exposed at low tide.
2. Most red algae consist of tightly packed filaments forming blades or branching segments. Some species develop feathery structures.
3. Red algae have chlorophyll a and chlorophyll b. Their red color is caused by the pigment **phycobilin** which is similar to certain blue green bacteria pigments.
4. Red algae store food in the form of **floridean starch**. Some also produce **agar.**
5. They have a complex life cycle involving 3 different types of body structures. Separate male and female algae produce gametes. Fertilization is by water.
6. **Polysiphonia** is a typical example of a feathery red algae common in marine waters. It occurs one of three kinds of thalli, a male gametophyte, female

gametophyte and tetrasporophyte, all finely branched and identical in appearance.

      a. The male sex structures or **spermatangia** of *Polysiphonia* resemble clusters of grapes. Each spermatangium functions as a nonmotile male gamete.

      b. Female sex structures, or **carpogonia** are produced on the female thallus. Each consists of a large single cell with a neck like structure called a **tricogyne** which functions as an egg. Fertilization occurs when a spermatangia enters the tricogyne and unites with the egg nucleus to form a zygote.

      c. The zygote develops into a carpospore which drifts in ocean currents.

7. Red algae such as nori and Irish Moss are harvested as food sources. It may be prepared or eaten raw or used for bulking agent as in the preparation of chocolate milk and other dairy products. Other uses include laxative, cosmetics, pharmaceutical preparations, adhesive, additive in water based paints, or an ingredient in laundry starch.

8. Many kinds of red algae are commercially valuable. **Agar,** the most widely used culture medium for cloning plants and growing animal cells is produced by red algae *Gelidium*. Agar is also used in preparation of bakery products, as a base for cosmetics, and an agent in the preparation of gelatin deserts.

Multiple Choice Self-Test

_____ 1. Green algae store food in the form of: (a) lipids (b) starches (c) fats (d) cellulose (e) amino acids (f) all of the above.

_____ 2. Ocean plankton is comprised mostly of: (a) red algae (b) brown algae (c) whales and other large animals (d) mostly green algae.

_____ 3. Parasitic protozoans lacking locomotory structures such as flagella belong to: (a) Ciliophora (b) Mastigophora (c) Sarcodina (d) Sporozoa.

_____ 4. *Euglena* uses this light receptor for orientation: (a) flagella (b) stigma (c) cell wall (d) contractile vacuole (e) pyrenoid body.

_____ 5. Food storage bodies in *Euglena* are termed: (a) starch bodies (b) glycogen (c) paramylin (d) vacuoles (e) a pellicle.

_____ 6. Red tides are caused by: (a) red algae (b) diatoms (c) Chrysophyta (d) dinoflagellates (e) Phaeophyta (f) all of the above.

_____ 7. The stipe of kelps is superficially similar to: (a) the fruits of an angiosperm (b) roots (c) the stem of vascular plants (d) all of the above.

_____ 8. These protists store oils and have cell walls impregnated with silicon: (a) Chrysophyta (b) Phaeophyta (c) Euglenophyta (d) Pyrophyta (e) all of the above.

_____ 9. Organisms in which the nucleic divide but the cell does not are termed:
(a) coenocytic (b) meiotic (c) mitotic (d) synctious (e) all of the above.

_____10. Red and brown algae most closely resemble plants in having: (a) cell walls
(b) roots (c) stems (d) leaves (e) chlorophylla

Concepts Self-Test

1. How do we distinguish between a colonial organism such as *Volvox* and a true multicellular organism such as a higher plant?

2. Describe the economic importance of the protistans to humans.

Label the life cycle of *Fucus*

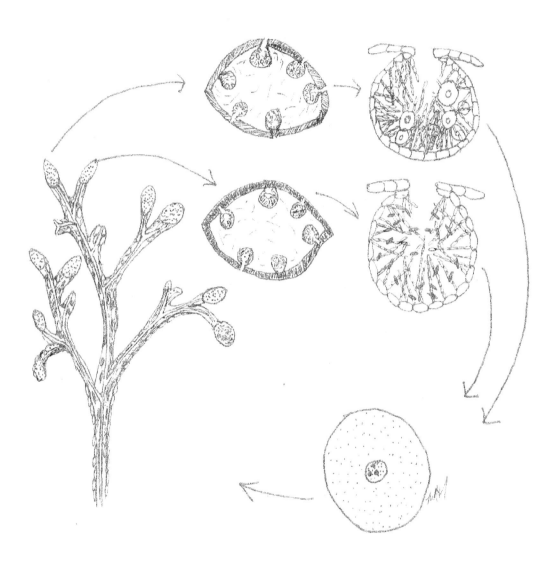

Visual Self-Test

Label the stages of the life cycle of Ulothrix.

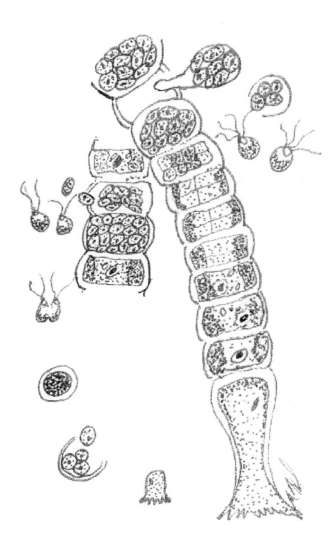

Visual Self-Test

Identify and label the following structures of *Spirogyra*: chloroplast, cell wall, pyrenoid, nucleus, cytoplasm, cytoplasmic strand, vacuole, conjugating canal, isogamete. Describe events that are happening and indicate the direction that these events take. Is this an example of sexual or asexual reproduction in *Spirogyra*?

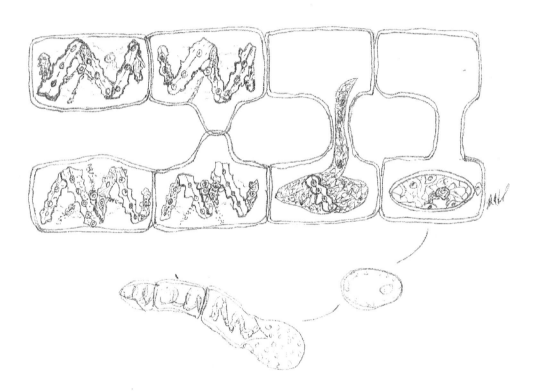

Chapter 19 The Fungi and Lichens

This chapter considers the following questions:
➤   What are the basic characteristics of fungi?
➤   What are the major groups of the fungi?
➤   What are typical representatives and life histories of the major groups of fungi?
➤   What is the economic importance of the fungi?
➤   What are the lichens?

I. Characteristics of the Fungi
A. General Information
   1. Fungi along with eubacteria are very important organisms that break down
       organic materials, thereby freeing them to be recycled into the bodies of
       new plants and animals. A common fungi along marine beaches called
       Corollospora martima helps decompose oil spills.
   2. Over 100,000 species of fungi are recognized and about 1,000 new species are
       discovered each year. Possibly another 200,000 species of fungi wait to be
       discovered.
   3. Most fungi consist of an intertwined mass of filamentous threads called **hyphae**
       which tend to branch freely or fuse together. The mass of hyphae of a
       fungi is called a **mycelium**.
   4. Some fungi seem to be closely related to prokaryotes. Others are considered to
       be more to eukaryotic plants. The slime molds may be advanced or
       aberrant protozoa. Each major group of fungi may have been separately
       derived from the protistans (that is, evolved from a different group).
   5. The fungi consist of five basic groups, slime molds, chytrids, water molds and
       true fungi.

II. Subkingdom Myxomcotineae- The Slime Molds
A. Introduction and Characteristics
   1. Slime molds are primitive, amoeba-like organisms that lack cell walls between
       adjacent cells. Instead, the slime mold consists of multinucleate body mass
       of protoplasm called a **plasmodia** which flows or creeps over damp leaves
       or debris and become converted to stationary **sporangia** containing
       globular **spores** that are particularly abundant in airborne dust.
   2. The 500 or so species of slime molds are yellow, orange, blue, violet, black,
       and colorless. Some botanists consider slime molds to be protistans.
   3. Habitats in which slime molds occur include old damp forest debris, under logs,
       on old shelf or bracket fungi, on older mushrooms and in moist areas
       with dead organic debris.

4. Slime molds move by slowly creeping over the surface at rate of 25 mm (about an inch) per hour. Feed on bacteria and other organic matter.

5. A slime mold typically contains several diploid nuclei which divide simultaneously. May increase size by 25 times in one week. Reproduction occurs when food is lacking. Several stalked sporangia may grow from the plasmodium or it may convert itself into a single large sporangia containing one celled **spores** which disperse throughout a jumbled mass of threads called a **capillitium**. Each spore consists of a single nucleus and a little cytoplasm surrounded by cell wall. 3 of 4 nuclei resulting from meiosis degenerate but the 4th an amoeboid cell **myxamoebae** (also called a swarm cell) emerges from the 4th. The swarm cells function as gametes with two swarm cells fusing in pairs to form a zygote from which the new plasmodium develops.

6. There are two kinds of slime molds, **regular slime molds** and **cellular slime molds**.

    a. **Regular slime molds** have a plasmodium as described above.

    b. **Cellular slime molds** do not produce true plasmodia. Instead, amoeba-like cells feed independently, dividing and producing new cells from time to time.

    c. When the population reaches certain size they stop feeding and clump together to form a **pseudoplasmodium**, which looks and crawls about rather like a garden slug and later transforms into sporangia-like masses of spores.

B. Human and Ecological Relevance of the Slime Molds

1. Ecologically, slime molds are decomposers like soil bacteria.

2. One species of slime molds causes powdery scab of potatoes, another causes disease of watercress.

3. Slime molds are often placed in the protistan group of organisms. That is, they greatly resemble colonial protozoans.

III. Subkingdom Chytridomycotineae- The Chytrids
A. General Information and Characteristics

1. The chytrids closely resemble brown algae from which they are thought to be derived. Chytrids range from single spherical cells to long, branching thread like hyphae.

2. Chytrids thrive on dead leaves, flowers, onion bulb scales, and other organic debris. They are considered to be the simplest of fungi. They are parasites of aquatic flowering plants, other aquatic fungi, algae, and amphibians.

3. Chytrids are typically colorless, spherical bodies that have short hyphae, are **coenocytic** (several nuclei within the protoplasm of a cell). Cell walls are impregnated with cellulose along with chitin.

4. Most reproduce sexually, developing **zoospores** within the spherical cell. The zoospores are motile gametes with haploid nuclei. They unite with two nonmotile cells and the diploid zygote nucleus undergoes meiosis. The zygote becomes a resting spore.

5. Little is known about the commercial or ecological importance of this group, but there is concern about chytrids causing the decline of tropical amphibian populations.

IV. Subkingdom Mastogomycotineae---- the Water Molds
A. General Information

1. Water molds are cottony fungal growths on fish where bruises and cuts develops. They are also aquatic fungi that grow on dead insects and other invertebrates.

2. Hyphae of water molds may branch repeatedly and form large coenocytic mycelia.

3. During asexual reproduction tips of some hyphae are separated by cross walls within which several biflagellate zoospores are produced. These emerge through a terminal pore to form the mycelia of new water molds.

4. Sexual reproduction involves oogonia and anteridia which form on side branches under influence of hormones. Mycelium is diploid and meiosis takes place in sex organs. Zygotes form in oogonia and eventually grow into new mycelia.

B. Ecological and Commercial Importance

1. Some water molds are serious diseases of plants.

2. **Downy Mildew** of grapes. Grows in dew and develops on grape leaves eventually killing the leaf, and ultimately the vine. Threatened the French wine industry in latter part of 19th century. Controlled by Bordeaux Mixture (copper sulfate and lime).

3. **Potato Blight** was responsible for the famous Irish potato famine of 1846 which destroyed several years of potato crops of Ireland. This led to the massive Irish immigration to America that took place during this time.

V. Subkingdom Eucomycotineae- the True Fungi
A. General Characteristics and Taxonomy

1. The true fungi are filamentous and lack motile cells. They produce hyphae and have cell walls comprised mostly of chitin. Variety of sexual reproduction. Food is digested by enzymes secreted outside fungi and then absorbed through cell walls.

2. There are three divisions of true fungi: the coenocytic true fungi (e.g. bread mold), the sac fungi (e.g. truffles) and the imperfect fungi (e.g. penicillin).

B. Division Zygomycota- the Coenocytic True Fungi

1. These are represented by *Rhizopus*, the black bread mold. Rhizopus spores are exceedingly common in the air, which explains why breads so easily get moldy.
2. When landing on a suitable substrate the *Rhizopus* spore quickly germinates and produces a coenocytic mycelium.
3. Asexual reproduction occurs when hyphae called **sporangiophores** grow upward from the mycelium producing globe shaped **sporangia** filled with black spores. Mature spores are released to be carried by air currents to other substrates.
4. Sexual reproduction is via conjugation in which hypha of one *Rhizopus* strain encounters hypha of another.
    - a. Each hypha strand has **gametangia** which grow and merge with one another, forming a large single multinucleate cell within which the nuclei of two stains unites.
    - b. A thick ornamented wall develops around this cell forming a **zygospore** which is released to undergo period of dormancy. Eventually, the zygospore splits and one or more sporangiosphores with sporangia at tips grow out. Meiosis produces spores.
5. *Pilobolus* is a true fungi that lives on dung. Spores are forcibly shot out of sporangia, adhere to grass and eaten by animals. Once spore passes through animal it germinates.
6. Human and Ecological Relevance of Coenocytic True Fungi
    - a. In Indonesia, bread mold is used to make a food called tempeh from boiled skinless soybeans inoculated with a bread mold and allowed to sit for 24 hours then is prepared fried, roasted or diced for soup.
    - b. Some bread molds are used to make Chinese cheese called sufu.
    - c. Species of bread mold are used in preparation of birth control pills, anesthetics, preparation of alcohols, and as a meat tenderizer.
    - d. The yellow pigment of another species colors margarine.

C. Division Eumycota

1. The 20,000 species of sac fungi are placed in the **Class Ascomycetes**.
2. The sac fungi include the yeasts, powdery mildews, brown fruit rots, truffles, ergot, and morels. Some sac fungi are parasites of insects. Others spoil fruit and are a bane to nurseries and orchards.
3. Unlike other fungi, most sac fungi are comprised of individual cells separated by cell walls.
4. Sexual reproduction involves formation of sacs (which give this decision its name) called **asci**.

a. When hyphae of two sexes become associated, male antheridia are formed on one and female ascogonia on the other.

b. Male nuclei migrate into ascogonium and pair with female nuclei but do not fuse.

c. The resulting new hyphae is called **asxogenous hyphae.**

d. Cells that grow from this asxogenous hyphae each contain one male and one female nucleus.

e. At maturity, pairs of nuclei unite and tubular ascia develop in a layer called **hymenium** at surface of structure called an **ascocarp**.

f. The now diploid zygote undergoes meiosis and produces 4 haploid nuclei, each of which divide mitotically to form 8 nuclei packed together in ascocarp which may be cup shaped, flask shaped or completely enclosed.

5. Asexual reproduction is by **conidia** (spores that are produced externally outside sporangium), either singly or in chains at tips of hyphae called **conidiophores**. Asexual reproduction in yeast is by **budding**.

6. Commercially, morels and truffles are among the most valuable sac fungi which are harvested for food. Truffles grow beneath oak trees. Although, prune like in appearance, truffles are actually the reproductive bodies of sac fungi.

7. **Ergot,** is a fungus that infects rye and other grains, causing serious crop damage. Ergot also produces powerful drugs which can cause ergotism in people that eat infected grains.

a. In humans ergot interferes with the central nervous system, causing hysteria, convulsions, death or gangrene of limbs.

b. Ergot is also poisonous to livestock that feed contaminated grains.

c. During the Middle Ages, outbreaks of ergot poisoning were common in Europe and may be the cause of people believing in witches.

d. In small controlled doses ergot is useful for stimulating contractions in child birth and in controlling migraines.

e. Ergot is the source of the hallucinogenic drug LSD.

8. Yeast are important ingredients in the preparation of baked goods and alcohol. Enzymes of yeasts aid in fermentation, raise bread dough, flavor wines, beers, ciders, and sake. Yeasts are also used in manufacture of drugs like ephedrine, as an additive in nose drops, and in treatment of asthma. Yeast is a rich source of Vitamin B. Yeast protein is also used as livestock feed.

9. Plant diseases caused by sac fungi species include Dutch Elm Disease and Chestnut Blight.

D. Class Basidiomycetes- the Club Fungi

1. The club fungi include the stink horns and mushrooms, toadstools, puffballs, earth stars, shelf fungi, bracket or shelf fungi, rusts, smuts, jelly fungi, and bird's nest fungi.
2. These fungi are called club fungi because they produce spores in the tips of swollen hyphae (called basidia) that resemble baseball bats or clubs.
3. The hyphae are divided into individual cells and each cell has either one or two nuclei. Cross walls between cells have a central pore surrounded by swelling and covered cap. Cap keep nuclei apart but allows cytoplasmic exchange.
4. Asexual reproduction is less frequent in club fungi. Some species bud, others asexually reproduce by fragmentation of hyphae which then develop into new individual club fungi.
5. Sexual reproduction begins when spore lands on suitable substrate, germinates and produces a mycelium just beneath surface.
    a. Cells of hyphae each contain a single haploid nucleus (these are termed **monokaryotic).**
    b. Monokaryotic mycelia of club fungi often occur in 4 mating types (types 1-4)
    c. Types 1-3 or 2-4 are able to mate with each other.
    d. If compatible mating types are brought together, the cells of each mycelium will unite, forming a new mycelium in which cells contain two nuclei (termed **dikaryotic**).
    e. When cells at the tip of dikaryotic hypha are ready to divide, a small protuberance appears on the side of cell and starts to grow downward. As it grows, a nucleus migrates into it from an adjacent hyphae and both nuclei then undergo mitosis simultaneously. A transverse wall forms, separating the daughter nuclei. When the process is completed the result is two cells.
    f. These dikaryotic mycelia may become dense and form a solid mass called a **button** which pushes to the surface and expands as a **basidiocarp** or mushroom.
6. Most mushrooms have a **cap** and a **stalk**. Some mushrooms have a ring-like structure called an annulus on the stalk and **gills** in the cap. The gills contain basidia. As each basidium matures two nuclei unite and undergo meiosis, producing 4 nuclei that become **basidiospores**.
7. Basidiospores have tiny pegs called **sterigmata** which serve as stalks for basidiospores.
8. Examples of Club Fungi include the following:
    a. **Shelf or Bracket Fungi**-grow out horizontally from bark or dead wood.

b. **Puffballs** are rounded ball-shaped fungi that produces spores in a parchment like membrane or basidiocarp. Usually edible and up to 4 feet in diameter.

c. **Earth Stars** resemble puffballs but have a ring-like set of petals around the base.

d. **Bird's Nest Fungus** grows on wood or manure, forming a nest-like cavity in which the basidiospores are the "eggs". Each "egg" has a long sticky thread. When rain drops strike the nest the "eggs" are splashed out of the nest and the the sticky thread catches on surrounding vegetation, whipping the "eggs" around and around. This spreads the spores over the whole area.

e. **Smuts** are an extremely important group of parasitic club fungi that damage corn, wheat, rye, and other grain crops. The mycelium of smuts grows between cells of host, absorbing nutriments and stimulating cells to grow large and divide forming tumors that eventually break open to release millions of tiny black spores. Some smuts affect flowering head, while others infect the whole plant.

f. **Rusts** are another extremely important group of fungal parasites that infect a wide variety of plants. Some have complex life cycles requiring two or more hosts.

g. **Black Stem Rust of Wheat** includes more than 300 known species. This rust has a complex life cycle involving two hosts, wheat and barberry plant to complete its life cycle.

9. **Human and Ecological Relevance of the Club Fungi**- of 25,000 species, only 75 are known to be poisonous. Unfortunately, these are common and hard to distinguish from good species.

    a. Many edible forms cause trouble if eaten with alcohol.

    b. **Death's Angel** is responsible for about 90% of mushroom caused fatalities. It take about 6-24 hours for poisoning to occur. Symptoms include intense stomach ache, blurred vision, vomiting, and eventually death.

    c. Some poisonous mushrooms have been used for centuries in religious ceremonies as hallucinogenic drugs and are still popular in Central America, e.g., *Teonanacatl* (Gods' flesh) mushrooms.

    d. The Black Forest or **Shitake** mushroom of China and Japan is a popular food. Grows naturally on oak logs and it is now widely cultured in the northwestern United States.

    e. Many mushrooms are very rich in phosphorous, calcium and iron. Contains lots of vitamin B, C, and D2(ergosterol).

    f. Mushrooms in general have high source of RNA which can retard the aging process.

g. Lentinacin--form shitake also lowers human cholesterol levels.

h. Shitake spores show antiviral activity against influenza, and polio viruses.

i. Extracts cause animal cells to produce the disease fighting drug called interferon.

10. Mushrooms have been cultivated since ancient times for food. *Agaricus bisporus* is cultivated in basements, caves and abandoned mines. The large operations use windowless warehouses, and a compost made of straw and horse or chicken manure.

E. Class Deuteromycetes- the Imperfect Fungi

1. The imperfect fungi includes all fungi in which the sexual stage of reproduction has not yet been identified or classified. Thus, this is really an artificial class within which are included some of the best known fungi.

2. All imperfect fungi reproduce by **conidia** and some parasitize protozoans and nematodes.

3. Among the many interesting imperfect fungi are the trapping fungi which have loops for snaring passing nematodes.

4. Human and Ecological Relevance of the Imperfect Fungi

a. *Penicillin* is surely the best known member of the imperfect fungi. It is used in the production of antibiotics. Also used to produce "smelly cheeses" such as blue, camembert, Roquefort, gorgonzola and Stilton.

b. *Aspergillus* is used to produce many products such as citric acid, effervescent salts, inks, medicines, chicle substitute, gallic acid, dyes, indelible black ink, artificial flavorings, perfume substances, chlorine, alcohols, plastics, toothpaste, soap, silvering of mirrors. It is also a source of soy obtained from soybeans.

c. *Aspergillus* also causes human diseases- infections of respiratory tract, and ears.

d. Other imperfect fungi cause familiar diseases such as "athletes foot," ringworm, white piedra (disease of beards and mustaches). Tropical species cause diseases of hands and feet. The disease called "Valley Fever" occurs in dryer areas of the United States and is caused by inhaled spores that produce lesions in the upper respiratory tract of lungs.

e. One form of imperfect fungi is used for the control of scale insects in Florida and California.

VI. The Lichens
A. General Information
1. Lichens were major sources of dyes in the past and are still commercially harvested for that purpose, although they are much less important now in the age of artificial dyes.
2. A lichen is actually a combination of two organisms, a fungus and an algae that are mixed together in spongy body called a thallus. They range in size from small to 1-2 meters.
3. Lichen provide an excellent example of symbiosis, or mutualism. The algae component produces food via photosynthesis for the fungi which in turn provides shelter and support for the algae and absorbs water and minerals from the soil.
4. About 25,000 species of lichens have been found. Most of the lichen fungi are sac fungi.
5. Lichens are hardy organisms that grow very slowly and may live up to 4,500 years. They are very tolerant of severe environmental conditions such as bare rocks. The gelatinous substance of their thallus enables them to withstand drying conditions. However, lichens are very sensitive to pollution and are used as criteria species to identify pollutants.
6. Both sexual and asexual reproduction occurs. Fungus produces ascocarps similar to ascocarps of sac fungi in which spores are continually produced. The allgae partner is produced by mitosis. About 1/3 of species form small powdery clusters of hyphae and algae called **soredia** which fragment from the thallus and are scattered by wind and rain.

B. Types and Body Structure of Lichens
1. Structurally, the thallus of the lichen consists of 3-4 layers of cells or hyphae. The surface is protected by an **upper cortex** in which hyphae are compressed, resembling a layer of parenchyma. The algae layer is just below the upper cortex. The medulla is interior to the algae layer and is comprised of loosely packed hyphae for food storage. A thinner **lower cortex** has anchoring rhizomes which glue the lichen to the substrate.
2. There are three basic types of lichen, crustose, foliose, and fruticose.
    a. **Crustose lichens** resemble a thin crust attached to substrate over the entire lower surface. Usually found on rocks.
    b. **Foliose lichens** have a leaf like thallus which overlaps others. Weakly attached to substrate. Edges frequently crinkly or divided into lobes.
    c. **Fruticose lichens** resemble miniature upright shrubs. Other species hang from branches in festoons from branches. Thalli are branched and cylindrical.

C. Ecological Relevance of Lichens

1. Many lichens are a food resource for reindeer, caribou, and livestock. Lichens are used as a food supplement in soups, bulking agent, and as a laxative.
2. Some species have antibiotic properties and are used to treat tuberculosis and as a salve for cuts and burns.
3. Greeks, Romans, and Native Americans used certain species as cloth dyes.

Multiple Choice Self-Test

_____ 1. Oomycetes of fungi contain ___ in their cell walls: (a) pectin (b) chitin (c) cellulose (d) glucose (e) starch (f) all of the above.

_____ 2. This group of fungi has flagellated gametes: (a) Ascomycota (b) Oomycota (c) Chytridiomycota (d) Zygomycota (e) all of the above.

_____ 3. These hyphae penetrate hosts of parasitic fungi: (a) mycorrhizae (b) haustoria (c) pectin (d) chitin (e) rhizoids (f) fruiting bodies.

_____ 4. Fungi food digestion occurs: (a) within cells (b) intracellularly (c) in nodes (d) extracellularly (e) in a digestive tract (f) in a fungi gut

_____ 5. Lichen symbiotic relationship includes a fungi and: (a) green algae (b) red algae (c) bacteria (d) virus (e) protozoan (f) all of the above.

_____ 6. Fruiting body of a basidiomycete is termed: (a) hyphae (b) basidia (c) gill (d) spore (e) sporangia (f) all of the above.

_____ 7. The zygospores produced by the bread mold are: (a) haploid (b) diploid (c) multinucleate (d) asexual (e) all of the above.

_____ 8. The dispersal and also dormant stage of most fungi: (a) spore (b) seed (c) hyphae (d) gamete (e) eggs (f) all of the above.

_____ 9. The different groups of fungi are distinguished on the basis of: (a) spores (b) locomotory structure (c) method of sexual reproduction (d) hyphal organization patterns (e) mode of obtaining nutrition.

_____ 10. Micorrhizae promote absorption of: (a) lipids (b) dirt (c) dissolved minerals (d) oxygen (e) water (f) all of the above.

_____ 11. Field mushrooms produce sexual spores in: (a) a basidium (b) an ascus (c) a sporophyte (d) a capsule (e) all of the above are correct.

Matching Self-Test

_____ 1. Dutch Elm Disease
_____ 2. Black Bread Mold
_____ 3. Plant rusts and smuts
_____ 4. Downy Mildew
_____ 5. Irish Potato Blight
_____ 6. Ergot
_____ 7. Breadmaker's yeasts

a. Ascomycota
b. Basidomycota
c. Chytridiomycota
d. Deuteromycota
e. Oomycota
f. Zygomycota

Concepts Self-Test

1. Describe benefits and problems with fungi relative to human food production and consumption using specific examples where applicable.

Visual Self-Test

Label the stages in the life cycle of this club fungi.

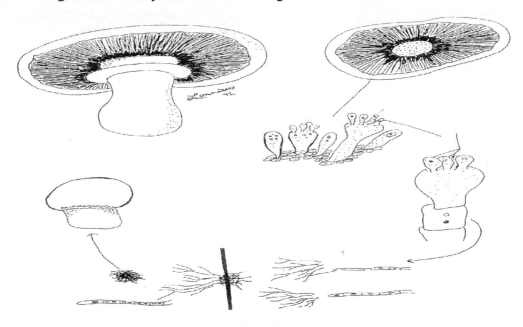

Visual Self-Test

Identify and label the components of this cross section of a lichen.

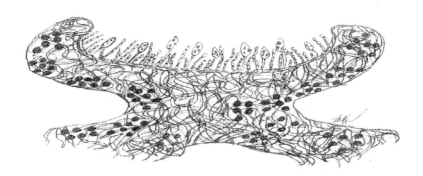

Chapter 20 Nonvascular Plants: The Bryophytes

This chapter considers the following questions:
- What are the bryophytes?
- How are the bryophytes intermediate between the algae and vascular plants?
- What are some of the important groups of bryophytes?

I. Introduction to the Nonvascular Plants
A. General Information
1. All eukaryotic plants share the same basic characteristics including having the same major pigments for photosynthesis---chlorophyll a, chlorophyll b, and carotenoids, storing food as starch, having cellulose in their cell walls, and developing phragmoplasts and cell plates. These common features suggest that all eukaryotic plants have the same ancestry.
2. Fossils reveal that the first eukaryotic plants appeared about 400 million years ago, presumably making the evolutionary transition from marine to fresh water habitats to land. Several factors were involved in adaptations to land environments.

B. Some Basic Adaptive Characteristics of Land Plants
1. Land plants have a fatty cuticle on the outside of the epidermis to protect their tissues against loss of water.
2. Land plants have a jacket of sterile tissue surrounding gametangia and spore producing cells.
3. The zygote of land plants develops into embryo within tissues that originally surround the egg.
4. Land plants typically produce their gametes in multicellular organs called gametangia.
5. Land plants typically exhibit greater structural organization and diversity than seen in other kingdoms of life. They also exhibit specializations of tissues and organs for support, photosynthesis, conduction, anchorage, reproduction, and protection.
6. Reproduction in bryophytes is primarily by sexual methods and the sporophyte stage is the dominant stage in bryophyte life history.

II. The Bryophytes
A. Introduction to the Division Bryophytes
1. Bryophytes are technically classed as nonvascular plants which are transitional or intermediate between the colonial algae and the higher vascular plants.

2. Bryophytes form green mats of vegetation covering on damp banks, trees, and shaded logs. They can occur from sea level to 18,000 ft. Some bryophytes are highly specialized and restricted to specific environments such as growing only on reindeer antlers or on the backs of large tropical insects.

3. All bryophytes have mycorrhizal fungi associated with their rhizoids.

4. Bryophytes lack xylem or phloem but have specialized vascular tissue called **hydroids** that occur in the center of stems along with food conducting cells called **leptoids** that surround the hydroids. Because they lack vascular tissue they are very soft and pliable.

5. The gametophyte generation is the dominant generation in bryophytes. The sporophyte generation remains attached to the ends of the gametophyte throughout its life.

6. Sexual reproduction involves fertilization by a flagellates sperm that is transported to the egg in water, therefore bryophytes occupy aquatic habitats such as ponds and wetlands.

7. Three classes of bryophytes are recognized, the **liverworts**, **hornworts**, and **mosses**.

III. Class Hepaticae-Liverworts
A. General Information

1. The 8,000 known species of liverworts develop directly from spores.

2. A liverwort consists mostly of a thin, flattened body called a thallus which is covered by an upper surface perforated by pores and lower surface of finger like rhizoids that anchor the liverwort to the substrate.

3. There are two basic kinds of liverworts, flattened (e.g. *Marchantia*) and leafy (e.g. *Porella*).

B. The Common Liverwort Marchantia

1. *Marchantia* commonly occurs on damp soil in fire-burned areas. The thallus of *Marchantia* is about 30 cells thick at center. *Marchantia* forks dichotomously as grows producing a branched thallus. Meristematic cells located at notches of the branches add new growth while older tissues located at the back or base of the liverwort decay.

2. Each *Marchantia* segment has many small pores opening into the interior. A section through Marchantia reveals interior cells of parenchyma apparently used for food storage. The bottom layer is an epidermis with rhizoids arising from it.

3. Asexual reproduction in *Marchantia* is by fragmentation

    a. Each fragment grows into a new *Marchantia*.

    b. Asexual reproduction also occurs when groups of cells produce tiny, lens-haped cups called **gemmae** on the upper surface of the thallus.

    c. Rain dislodge gemmae grow into new *Marchantia* thallus.

4. Sexual reproduction in *Marchantia* involves the production of specialized male gametangia called **antheridiophores** and female gametangia called **archegoniophores**. The male and female gametangia are produced on separate gametophytes, and extend just above the surface of the thallus.

5. The male antheridiophore is disc-like with a scalloped margin. Antheridia containing sperm are produced in rows just beneath the upper surface.

6. The female archegonia are flask-like and contain a single female egg. They are arranged in rows and hang neck down beneath the spokes of archegoniophore. Each has an entrance channel called the neck canal. The neck of the canal opens when the egg is mature.

7. When it rains the flagellated (and haploid) sperm swim to the neck of the archaegonia and enter to fertilize the egg within.

8. The resulting diploid zygote develops a multicellular **embryo** which is the immature sporophyte.

    a. The sporophyte remains anchored in the tissues of the archegoniophore by means of knob-like **foot** which in turn hangs suspended by stalk called a **seta**.

    b. Thus, the sporophyte is entirely parasitic, growing from the undersurface of the archegoniophore of the female plant, that is, the female gametophyte which partially surrounds the sporophyte with a protective **perianth**.

9. The body of the sporophyte is termed a **capsule**. It consists of a foot, the seta, and a sporangium in which spores are produced.

    a. At maturity, spore mother cells in the sporangium undergo meiosis to produce haploid spores when then multiply by mitosis to produce hundreds of spores.

    b. Other cells within the sporangium develop spring-like elaters that twist and untwist in response to changes in humidity, dispersing spores.

10. When the spores germinate they produce the new gametophyte generations. Separate male and female gametophytes will be produced in the new gametophyte generation.

C. Leafy Liverworts

1. Leafy liverworts are common in tropical jungles.
2. Their body mass consists of two rows of partially overlapping thalli.
3. Liverworts have folds and lobes that form little water traps that animals drink out of.
4. Some liverworts may function like pitcher plants and eat insects that drink the entrapped water.

IV. Class Anthocerotae- the Hornworts
A. General Information

1. There are about 100 species of hornworts worldwide. All are tiny and grow on moist soils in shaded areas or on trees.
2. Hornworts get their name from their sporophyte which resembles a miniature cattle horn.
3. Hornworts have a gametophyte thallus similar to liverworts which is anchored by rhizoids to the substrate. They differ from liverworts in having only one large chloroplast in each cell. Like *Spirogyra*, the hornworts store starch in pyrenoids in each chloroplast.
4. The muscilaginous hornwort cells support populations of blue-green bacteria.
5. Asexual reproduction in hornworts is by fragmentation of lobes from the thallus.
6. Sexual reproduction occurs in the gametophyte generation when archegonia and antheridia are produced in rows beneath the surface of gametophyte. Some plants are bisexual and others unisexual. Sporophytes have numerous stomata and no setae. A meristem above the foot continually increases length of sporophyte from base. As growth occurs, spore mother cells surrounding a central rod like axis in the sporophyte horn splits into two or three ribbon like segments, releasing spores.

V. Class Musci- Mosses
A. General Information

1. 15,000 species of mosses are known, including true mosses, peat mosses, and rock mosses.
2. Many plants that are named mosses such as Spanish Moss and Club Moss are not really mosses. Instead, they are types of lichens.
3. The moss plant begins as a flattened, alga-like protonema. As it grows it produces rhizoids to anchor the plant and "buds" which develop into "stems" from which "leaves" arise. The moss plant is called a thallus.
4. The thallus differs from true leaves of higher plants such as flowering plants in lacking mesophyll, stomata or veins. The leaf-like blades of mosses have midrib and cells with lens-shaped chloroplasts.
5. In peat mosses, the leaves consist largely of large water storage cells interspersed with green photosynthetic cells.
6. The leaves are formed in three ranks and appear to be spiraled along a central axis. The axis is stem-like but does not have xylem or phloem.
7. In some mosses water is transported by special cells called hydroids. In others water is transferred from cell to cell by capillary action. Because they lack an efficient transport system for water and nutrients, the mosses are always small plants.
8. The gametophyte generation is dominant. The sporophyte generation is parasitic and develops at or near the apex of the thallus.

9. **Sexual Reproduction** begins with the formation of multicellular gametangia on the leafy shoots of the gametophyte.
   a. In most species both male and female **gametangia** are produced on same plant. Some species have separate male and female gametophyte plants.
   b. The female archegonium is cylindrical and projects upward from the fertile tips, or apex of the gametophyte.
   c. Cells in the enlarged ventral portion of archegonium (called a **venter**) produce a single **egg**.
   d. That part of the archegonium above the venter tapers into a long, narrowing neck containing a **canal** through which the sperm will travel.
   e. Male gametangia called antheridia, are borne on short stalks within which are produced masses of sperm cells. During and following rainstorms water enters the antheridia activating the flagellated sperm.
   f. Sperm swim down the canal and unite with egg inside the venter to form a **zygote** that grows rapidly into an embryo.
   g. The zygote attaches to the stem of the gametophyte by a swollen knob-like **foot**.
   h. The embryo is actually the developing sporophyte which grows into a capsule called a **calyptra** topped by an **operculum**.
   i. Within the calyptra spore mother cells undergo meiosis, producing millions of haploid spores which escape through an opening called **peristome**.
   j. In some mosses, the capsule splits open and the spores are blown away in wind.
   k. Each spore produces a green tubular thread of cells called a **protonema** which grows into the gametophyte, producing leaf-like buds from along its length and rhizoids at its base,
   l. This completes the life cycle of the moss.
10. **Asexual Reproduction** occurs by fragmentation of vegetative parts of gametophytes. Each fragment develops into a new gametophyte.

B. Human and Ecological Relevance of Mosses
1. Many mosses are pioneers that colonize bare areas and become soil builders. Mosses are ecologically important because they help retain soil moisture, reduce flooding and erosion, and provide soil packing material.
2. The peat mosses are extensively used in nurseries for potting mixtures. They are so efficient that two pounds of peat moss will absorb 55 pounds of water.

Multiple Choice Self-Test

_____ 1. Which are bryophytes: (a) mosses and ferns (b) mosses and club mosses (c) mosses and hornworts (d) ferns, horsetails, and hornworts.

_____ 2. Life cycle generation that is dominant in the bryophytes: (a) gametophyte (b) sporophyte (c) diploid (d) all of the above.

_____ 3. Liverwort cells obtain water via: (a) through conducting tissue (b) through a network of rhizomes (c) from the air or adjacent cells (d) directly through leaves (e) all of the above are correct.

_____ 4. This structure regulates the release of spores: (a) elater (b) foot (c) peristome (d) calyptra (e) operculum (f) all of the above.

_____ 5. Mosses substitute these structures for xylem: (a) elaters (b) setae (c) sieve elements (d) leptoids (e) hydroids (f) all of the above.

_____ 6. Asexaul reproduction by talloid liverworts is by: (a) conidia (b) rhizomes (c) hyphae (d) emmae (e) soredia (f) all of the above.

_____ 7. Structure that protects the free end of the moss sporophyte capsule: (a) operone (b) operculum (c) pericycle (d) peristome (e) all of the above.

_____ 8. Liverwort cells obtain water via: (a) via rhizoids (b) via conducting tissue (c) from air (d) from bacteria (e) all are correct.

_____ 9. Mosses have which of the following: (a) root hairs (b) true leaves (c) stems (d) archegonia (e) all of the above (f) none of the above.

_____10. The life cycle of mosses includes: (a) flowering structures (b) spores produce protonemeta (c) the seed is naked, as in gymnosperms (d) gemmae produce spores (e) the gametophyte depends on the sporophyte for support (f) all of the above.

_____11. A basic difference between bryophytes and tracheophytes: (a) the gametophyte generation is dominant (b) the sporophyte generation is dominant (c) bryophytes lack a true vascular system (d) bryophytes have a vascular system (e) all of the above (f) none of the above.

Concepts Self-Test

1. Where would you go to collect or at least observe mosses and other bryophytes in the field? Why?

Label the stages of the moss life cycle and the structures in each stage. Label the
gametophyte and sporophyte stages in this illustration.

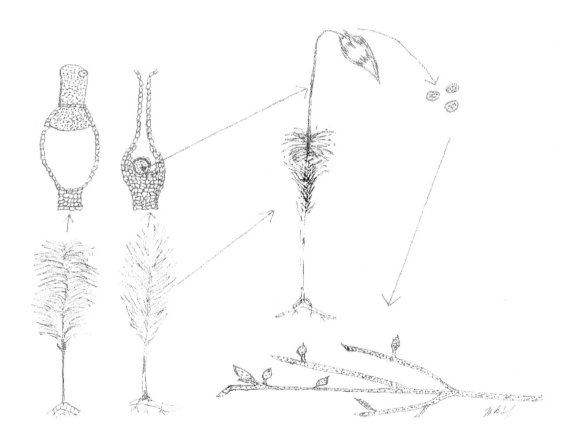

Chapter 21 Ferns and Fern Relatives

This chapter considers the following questions:
➤   What groups of plants are considered the close relatives of ferns?
➤   What are the life cycles of ferns and their allies?
➤   What are ferns and how are they related to other plants?

I. Vascular Plants
A. General Information

1. In order for terrestrials plants to attain size and become upright they had to evolve stems and leaves. This required the development of a conduction system for water and food.
2. Thus, the vascular plants all have a system of roots, stems, and leaves.
3. In the vascular plants, the sporophyte generation is the predominant generation while the gametophyte generation is the small and often "parasitic" on the sporophyte plant.
4. The vascular plants include two groups, the nonseed vascular plants that produce spores and the seed vascular plants that produce seeds. The nonseed vascular plants include the whisk ferns, club mosses, quillworts, scourging rushes, horsetails, and true ferns.
5. Vascular plants can be further classed on the basis of the type of spore they produce into **homosporous** or **heterosporous** types.
6. Vascular plants that produce a single kind of spore are called **homosporous**. The spores develop into gametophytes bearing both male antheridia and female archegonia. Almost all true ferns, whisk ferns, club mosses, and horsetails are homosporous.
7. Vascular plants that produce two kinds of spores are called **heterosporous**. Heterosporous plants produce two distinct kinds of sporangia, female megaspores and male microspores. Both types actually develop within the wall of the sporangia.
8. The sporophyte is therefore dominant generation and the gametophyte is a "parasitic growth" on the sporophyte.
9. Most ferns, club mosses, and all seed plants (all higher plants) are examples of heterosporous plants in which the gametes are different in size.

II. Division Psilophyta--- the Whisk Ferns
A. General Information

1. The whisk ferns are the simplest of all vascular plants. The dominant generation is the sporophyte and the whisk fern is a sporophyte plant that lack true leaves and roots. Instead, a whisk fern consists of a series of stems and rhizomes that fork evenly.
2. Relationships of the whisk ferns are unclear but they may be related to extinct plants called **Psilophytales** that were common about 40 million years ago.
3. Whisk ferns are found in tropical and subtropical regions of the world. In the United States they are found in Florida, Louisiana, Texas, Arizona and Hawaii. Whisk ferns are extensively cultivated in Japan.

B. Form and Function of Whisk Ferns

1. The simple, dichotomously branching stem of a whisk fern arises from an underground rhizome. Photosynthesis occurs in the epidermis.
2. Conduction is via a central column of star shaped xylem surrounded by phloem (the central column of conduction tissue is called a **stele**). Layers of parenchyma and sclerenchyma tissue surrounds the stele and forms the cortex of the whisk fern.
3. Whisk ferns are homosporous and exhibit alternation of generation.
4. Spores are produced in sporangia located at the ends of branches of the sporophyte.
   - a. Growth of the spore produces a colorless, miniature gametophyte that lives in soil, on trees or other suitable substrate and obtains nutrients as a saprobe.
   - b. Mature gametophytes produce archegonia and antheridia on their surface.
   - c. Flagellated sperm from the antheridia swim to the archegonia and fertilize the egg, producing a diploid zygote.
   - d. The embryo sporophyte grows from the zygote.
   - e. At first the embryo remains attached to the gametophyte archegonia but as it continues to grow a rhizome develops at one end and a shoot at the other end.
   - f. The sporophyte detaches from the gametophyte to live on its own.
   - g. As the sporophyte continues to grow, mycorrhizae attach to the underground rhizome while the shoot branches to form the shoot of the whisk fern complete with sporangia.
5. Cells of mature sporangia meiotically produce spores to start the life cycle again.

III. Division Lycophyta- the Club Mosses and Quillworts
A. General Information
1. The club mosses and quillworts number about 950 species that are very widely distributed.
2. 300 million years ago, during the Carboniferous period, tree-like forms of club mosses dominated the world's forests. Coal and oil deposits from that evolutionary period are fossil remains of these plants.
3. Today, the surviving club mosses are typically small plants belonging to one of three groups, the ground pines and ground cedars (*Lycopodium species*) which grow on forest floors, the spike mosses (*Selaginella*) and the quillworts (*Isoetes*) of wetland habitat.

B. Structure and Life History
1. Structurally, the club mosses and quillworts consist of either a simple prostrate or upright stem covered with miniature leaves called microphylls. The plant is anchored by rhizomes.
2. Ground pines consist of a simple sporophyte that may be branched or unbranched. They are generally small, but some tropical forms are a meter or more in height.
3. Asexual reproduction occurs via development of adventitious roots on rhizome, which may become independent plants.
4. Sexual reproduction is more complex.
>   a. Bean shaped sporangia are produced on a modified leaf call a sporophyll.
>   b. Clusters of these sporangia form cone-like structures called **strobili**.
>   c. Spore mother cells in the sporangia undergo meiosis producing spores that are carried away by wind.
>   d. When a spore germinates, it produces a carrot-like gametophyte.
>   e. The gametophyte may live for several years, producing archegonia and antheridia which produce eggs and sperm.
>   f. Fertilization produces a zygote that develops into a foot, stem and leaves which continues to grow, eventually producing the mature club moss.

C. *Selaginella*- Spike Mosses
1. The 700 species of spike mosses differ from ground pines in two ways:
>   a. their leaves have a tiny tongue like appendage called a **ligule**.
>   b. they are **heterosporous**, producing two kinds of spores.

2. Sexual reproduction resembles that of ground pines.
    a. The sporophyte produces a microsporangia and a female megasporangia that produces megaspores.
    b. Each megasporangia produces 4 megaspores.
    c. Each microspore develops into a male gametophyte and each megaspore develops into a female gametophyte.
    d. Flagellated male gametes fertilize female gametes that ultimately produce a sporophyte.
    e. The sporophytes is a separate plant, as ground pines.
3. Ancient relatives of club mosses and ground pine were dominant 30 meter tall trees of Devonian and Carboniferous forests and coal swamps.

D. *Isoetes-* Quillworts
1. The sporophytes of the 60 species of quillworts are small, generally less than 100 millimeters tall, and have spoon shaped leaves arranged in a tight spiral on a stubby stem. The rhizome of a quillwort has vascular cambium and may live many years.
2. Reproduction in quillworts is very similar to that in spike mosses with heterosporous sporangia produced at base of leaves.

IV. Division Sphenophyta- The Horsetails and Scouring Rushes
A. General Information
1. The 25 species of horsetail and scouring rushes have ribbed stems containing silica deposits and whorled scale like microphylls for leaves. Most are small to medium sized plants but some grow up to 2 to 6 meters in height. *Equisetum* is a common streamside horsetail.
2. The sporophyte consists of an upright stem with branches and whorls of scale like leaves called microphylls occurring at nodes along the stem where photosynthesis occurs.

B. Structure and Reproduction
1. Horsetail stems are ribbed and exhibit well defined nodes and internodes. Silica deposits in the stems provide protection. The concentration of silica gives horsetails their common name of scouring rushes.
2. The upright stems grow from a horizontal rhizome and a horsetail colony may be derived from a single rhizome---this is an example of plant cloning.
3. In cross section the stem has a pith in the center that eventually breaks down, leaving a central hollow cavity. Rings of smaller canals surround the pith. **Carinal canals** on the inner rings transport water and minerals. Each carinal canal has a patch of xylem and phloem. Air-filled **vallecular canals** form an outer ring which is arranged between ribs.

4. Asexual reproduction occurs via fragmentation; if stems and rhizomes are broken up by storm, each fragment is capable of producing new sporophyte plants.
5. Horsetails are heterosporous. Sexual reproduction occurs on special stems that arise from rhizomes in spring which bear **strobili** in form of cones. The outer surface of each strobili is covered with hexagonal plates and resembles the surface of honeycomb. Each hexagon contains a sporangiophore with 5-10 sporangia attached to inner surface of rim that produce spores. Each spore has 4 ribbon like **elaters** at one pole.
6. Spores are dispersed in the wind currents. As spore is carried on wind, elaters act like wings until they hit a humid air pocket, then elaters coil around spore which drops to ground.
7. Germination of the spore produces a small, lobed gametophyte anchored by rhizoids.

V. Division Pterophyta- The Ferns
A. General Information and Taxonomy

1. The 11,000 species of ferns are important plants in natural ecosystems where they provide food for wildlife. They are mostly small to medium sized plants but some tropical species may reach 20 meters in height. They are abundant in wetter tropical habitats of the world.
2. Ferns are common ornamentals. Fronds are used for food and medicine sources.
3. The sporophyte is the dominant generation and represented by the fern. The gametophyte consists of a small vegetative plant called a **prothallus**.

B. Structure and Reproduction

1. All ferns consist of one or more leaves arising from a stem in the form of a rhizome. Fern leaves are megaphylls and are called fronds. They are almost always highly divided.
2. There are two types of fronds, vegetative or sterile, which are the main organs of photosynthesis and reproductive fronds, which are involved in sexual reproduction.
3. Fronds begin as tightly coiled leaves called **fiddleheads** or **crosiers** which grow and unfold.
4. Sexual reproduction begins with the formation of sporangia on under surface of the reproductive frond.
   a. Inside the sporangia, spore mother cells undergo meiosis to produce either 48 or 64 spores per sporangium.
   b. Sporangia usually grow in small clusters called **sori** which are protected by an umbrella-like flaps of tissue called **indusia** in some species.

       c. Each sporangia consists of a row of cells on one end called an
          annulus.

       d. Turgor changes in cells of the annulus causes it to open and
          disperse spores.

    5. Spores are carried by wind to wet habitats, germinate and produce green,
      heart-shaped called prothalli that are anchored by rhizomes.

    6. The prothallus produces antheridia interspersed along the apex and archegonia
      near the notch. Gametes unite to form the zygote which grows into the
      sporophyte fern.

Multiple Choice Self-Test

_____ 1. The fern sori consists of: (a) clusters of pinnae (b) clusters of rhizomes
      (c) clusters of sporangia (d) clusters of sporophytes.

_____ 2. Vascular plants: (a) produce seeds (b) are heterosporous (c) have a dominant
      sporophyte generation (d) all are correct.

_____ 3. These flaps of tissue protect the developing sporangia of ferns: (a) sori
      (b) indusia (c) elators (d) calyptra (e) opercula (f) all of the above.

_____ 4. Spike mosses differ from other groups in being: (a) homosporous (b) asexual
      (c) heterosporous (d) all of the above (e) none of the above.

_____ 5. Whisk ferns lack roots and? (a) leaves (b) stems (c) sexual cells (d) all of the
      (e) none of the above.

_____ 6. Rhizoids are usually produced in the fern: (a) thallus (b) sexual cells
      (c) gametophyte (d) sporophyte (e) all of the above.

_____ 7. The fern sori consists of clusters of: (a) sporangia (b) rhizomes (c) sex
      cells (d) sporangia (e) sporophytes (f) sporophylls.

_____ 8. In ferns the gametes unite to produce a: (a) algae (b) sporophyte (c) conifer
      (d) gametophyte (e) all of the above (f) none of the above.

_____ 9. The ferns were the dominant terrestrial plant form during: (a) they are dominant
      now (b) the Mesozoic (c) the Carboniferous (d) the last 100 years.

_____10. These edible structures are the young leaves of ferns: (a) anthredia
      (b) fiddleheads (c) rhizomes (d) prothalli (e) all of the above.

Visual Self-Test

Label the stages in the fern life cycle illustrated below. Which is the gametophyte and which is the sporophyte stage?

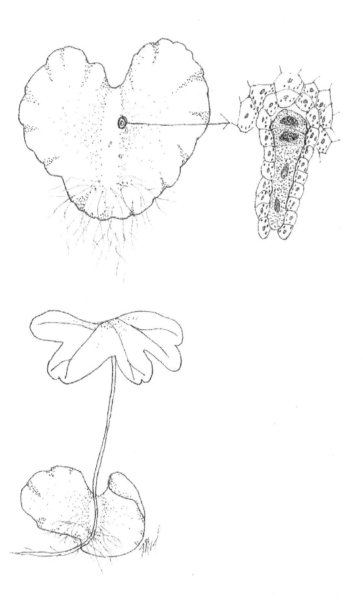

Visual Self-Test

Identify and label the structures in this cross section of a fern sori.

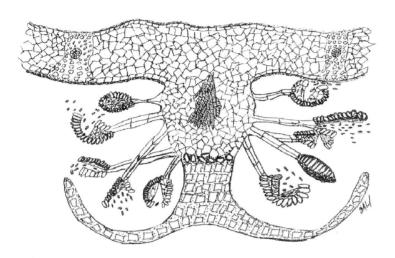

Visual Self-Test

Identify and label the structures in this cross section. What is it?

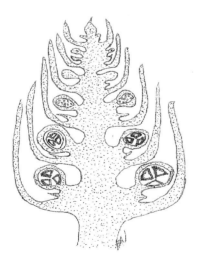

Chapter 22 The Gymnosperms

This chapter considers the following questions:
➢   What are the seed vascular plants?
➢   What are the gymnosperms?
➢   How do gymnosperms differ from lower vascular plants?
➢   How do gymnosperms differ from the angiosperms?
➢   What are the major characteristics and life cycles of gymnosperms?
➢   What are the ecological and commercial values of gymnosperms?

I. Seed Vascular Plants
A. General Information
1. Seed vascular plants differ from all other plants in producing seeds for dispersion as opposed to spores or other types of propagule.
2. The seed is the embryo of the next generation of plants. Seeds are an important adaptation for plants for invading land. Seeds have protective seed coat and supply of food (usually endosperm) to nourish embryo growth during the germination period.
3. Seeds provide a major adaptive advantage for seed plants, allowing them to remain dormant during unsatisfactory climate conditions such as cold and snow, or lack of moisture. This survival value of seeds is of major importance in the evolution of seed plants.
4. All seed plants have a vascular conduction system of xylem and phloem.
5. All seed plants have alternation of generation and are heterosporous.
   a. The male microspore gives rise to pollen which represents the male gametophyte.
   b. The female megaspore is the embryo sac on the sporophyte.
   c. Fertilization results in the diploid sporophyte plant.
6. The sporophyte is the dominant generation. The gametophyte generation is very small and remains attached to the sporophyte plant, developing within sporophyte tissue.
7. The two taxonomic classes of seed plants are the **gymnosperms** and **angiosperms**.

II. The Gymnosperms
A. Introduction
1. The gymnosperms are the most primitive seed plants. The earliest gymnosperms date from the Devonian of 250 million years ago. Most modern gymnosperms are trees or shrubs.
2. They produce naked seeds, meaning that the seeds are on sporophylls instead of being enclosed within fruits as in flowering plants.
3. Female sporophylls are often spirally arranged in female strobili (cones) which develop on the sporophyte along with smaller male strobile which produces **pollen grains**. The female gametophyte is produced within an **ovule** containing a fleshly nutritive diploid **nucellus** that is itself encased in one or more layers of diploid tissue. These outer layers constitute an **integument** which becomes the **seed coat** after fertilization and embryo development.
4. The sporophytes of gymnosperms are normally trees and the gametophyte is even more reduced than in ferns. The gametophyte is not free living but part of the sporophyte.
5. Taxonomically, the gymnosperms include four important divisions, the conifers, cycads, ginkos, and gnetophytes.

B. Commercial and Ecological Importance of Gymnosperms
1. The gymnosperms are second only to flowering plants in their commercial importance. They are a major source of construction lumber (pines for framing, firs for flooring, cedars for fence posts and cedar lined closets and furniture), pulp for newsprint, and plastics.
2. Resin products of gymnosperms include turpentine, methanol, varnishes, printing ink, and perfumes. Other products include dyes from hemlock, tannins for shoe leather, flavoring from berries and incense.
3. The inner bark and seeds of some gymnosperms are harvested for food.
4. Gymnosperms are used as landscape ornamentals and Christmas trees.
5. An important anti-cancer drug is extracted from the Western Yew.

III. Division Coniferophyta- the Conifers
A. General Information
1. There are about 575 species of conifers.
2. The conifers include the pines, firs, spruces, hemlocks, redwoods, cedars.
3. The conifers are an ancient group that date from the Carboniferous.

B. Pines- *Pinus*
1. *Pinus* is the largest genus of pines.
2. *Pinus* are mostly trees of large coniferous forests of the northern hemispheres

3. The pines include the world's oldest living organisms. The Bristlecone Pine of the western United States, for example may live nearly 5,000 years.

4. The leaves of pines are needle-like and are arranged in clusters or bundles of 2 to 8 needles per bundle. Each cluster of needles is called a cylindrical bundle or **fascicle**.

5. Pines occur in areas where the topsoil is frozen part of year so water is often unavailable for long periods of time. Some species also occur in dry and windy landscapes where water loss is always a problem.

6. Pines are able to tolerate dry conditions only because their needle leaves have several important adaptations to conserve water:
   - a. The **hypodermis** consists of several layers of thick walled cells.
   - b. The epidermis has a thick cuticle for water proofing.
   - c. The stomata are sunken and surrounded by an endodermis.
   - d. Mesophyll cells do not have air spaces between them as in other plants.

7. Pines also have **resin canals** in mesophyll and also in other parts of plant that secrete **resin**. Resin is an aromatic and antiseptic insecticide and fungicide that deters insects and prevents fungal invasion of the plant.

8. The xylem of pines consist only of tracheids--- there are no vessel elements or fibers. Because pine lacks thick-walled vessel elements, the wood is soft and pines are called softwoods while angiosperms are called hardwoods.

9. The phloem lacks companion cells but other cells called **albuminous cells** apparently perform the same function. Roots may be associated with mycorrhizal fungi.

10. Sexual reproduction in conifers involves the production of heterospores, the smaller male microspores and the larger female megaspores.
   - a. Microspores in microsporangia develop in pairs towards bases of scales and are arranged in a spiral or in whorls around an axis forming a strobilus or male cone. Microspore mother cells undergo meiosis and develop into 4 haploid microspores which develop into pollen grains (each consisting of four cells and a pair of external sacs which function in dispersion).
   - b. Megaspores are produced in megasporangia located in the female cones. They are usually produced on upper branches of the same tree as the male. Female cones are larger and more complex than male cones.
   - c. Each ovule has one **megasporangia** within a multicellular nutritive tissue called the **nucellus**. This is in turn surrounded by a thick layered **integument.**
   - d. The integument has a channel called a **micropyle** that opens toward the center of the cone. One of the integument layers later becomes the **seed coat** of seed.

e. A single megaspore mother cell within the nucellus of each ovule undergoes meiosis to produce a row of large megaspores. All but one degenerate. The survivor develops and grows and is the female gametophyte. Over several months it produces 2-6 archegonia, each becoming differentiated at the end of microphyle.

f. Each archegonium contains a single egg.

g. Female cones take two seasons to mature. During first spring they appear reddish and mature with scales spread apart. At this time pollen grains carried by wind sift down between scales and catch on sticky drops of fluid **pollen drops** oozing from the micropyle to the top of the nucellus.

h. After fertilization, the scales of the cone close, protecting the developing ovule.

i. About a month after pollination, meiosis occurs and the megaspores are formed. The female gametophyte does not mature with archegonia for another year. The pollen grains form a **pollen tube** which slowly digests its way through nucellus to the area where the archegonia will form.

j. As the pollen tube grows, two of the 4 original cells enter it. One, the **generative cell** divides and forms 2 or more **sterile cells** and a **spermatogenous cell**. The latter divides to produce sperm. The pollen tube and its sperm is the male gametophyte of the gymnosperm (no separate antheridium plant is formed).

k. About 15 months after pollination the tube reaches the now mature archegonium.

l. Sperm in the pollen tube unite with the egg to form a zygote.

m. Each zygote develops into **embryo** and an outer integument layer that hardens to form the seed coat.

n. A membranous layer of the cone scale becomes the wing on each seed to aid dispersal.

o. Squirrels help by opening cones. In some species such as the Lodgepole Pine, Jack Pine, and Knob Cone Pine, the cones remain closed until seared by fire, then they open to release seeds. This is called serotiny.

IV. Division Cycadophyta- The Cycads
A. General Information

1. The cycads number about 100 species of gymnosperms that have palm like leaves but produce seeds in cones. They are slow growing tropical species that resemble tree ferns and palms. Some cycads are used as household and landscaping ornamentals.

2. The cycads have unbranched trunks up to 15 meters tall surmounted by a crown of large pinnately divided leaves. Extinct cycadenoids were dominant plants of Mesozoic.
3. The life cycle of cycads resembles that of conifers but are dioecious with separate male and female plants. They are unique gymnosperms because they have flagellated sperm.

V. Division Ginkgophyta- The Ginkgos

1. This gymnosperm taxon consists of a single living species. *Gingko biloba*.
2. Ginkgos were once widely distributed and primarily northern. They are called maidenhair trees because their leaves resemble the pinnae of maidenhair ferns. The leaves lack midribs.
3. *Ginko biloba* has fan shaped leaves and seeds in fleshy and very smelly coverings.
4. The ginkgos are dioecious with life cycle like that of the cycads. The plum like seeds are enclosed in a fleshy coating that is strongly odoriferous to attract flies for pollination. Because of strong odor, male trees are preferred as landscape plants.

VI. Division Gnetophytes

1. The 70 species of gnetophytes belong to 3 genera, the *Ephedra, Gnetum*, and *Welwitschia*.
2. Gnetophytes share some characteristics with angiosperms including the presence of woody vessels in xylem and flower like strobili.
3. *Ephedra*, a shrubby plant of the western desert, is a North American representative of this division. Photosynthesis occurs in *Ephedra* stems. *Ephedra* is also well known as the source of Mormon tea. A derivative called ephedrine is used in treatment of asthma.
4. *Gnetum* occurs in the tropics of South America, Africa , and Southeast Asia. Most are vine-like.
5. Welwitschia is also called the century plant and occurs only in the Namib and Mossamedes deserts of southwestern Africa. Plants carry on CAM photosynthesis and stomata open only at night. Plants survive mostly on dew.
   a. The stem is short and cup-like with a large taproot. Old plants develop a crusty bark-like covering on surface of stem.
   b. Male and female strobili are produced on separate plants.

Multiple Choice Self-Test

_____ 1. The conifer leaf is specialized for existence in: (a) cool and wet conditions (b) dry conditions (c) tropical conditions (d) all of the above.

_____ 2. The gymnosperms depend primarily on ___ for dispersal: (a) wind (b) water (c) waves (d) insects and other animals.

_____ 3. Fertilization in conifers is primarily by: (a) the wind (b) water carried seeds (c) bats (d) hummingbirds (e) all of the above.

_____ 4. Seed evolution probably arose as an adaptation to: (a) polar climates (b) arid climates (c) dominance by the gametophyte generation

_____ 5. The dominant generation in gymnosperms is the: (a) the asexual generation (b) sporophyte (c) gametophyte (d) flowering generation.

_____ 6. Both pines and cycads have: (a) seed cones (b) palmlike leaves (c) flagellated sperm (d) homosporous conditions (e) all of the above.

_____ 7. The seed coat of a pine seed comes from the: (a) seed (b) pollen grain (c) egg (d) integument (e) all of the above (f) none of the above.

_____ 8. How many seasons does it take for a female pine cone to mature: (a) one (b) two (c) three (d) four (e) five.

Visual Self-Test

Describe the events that are occurring in the development of this pollen grain.

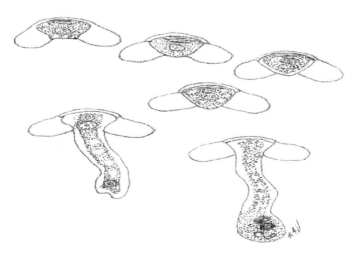

Chapter 23 The Flowering Plants

This chapter considers the following questions:
- What are the angiosperms?
- What is the structure and life cycle of a typical angiosperm?
- How does pollination occur in angiosperms?
- What is double fertilization in angiosperms?
- How do the great groups of angiosperms-the monocots and dicots-differ?
- What are some of the major families of angiosperms?

I. Division Anthophyta- The Flowering Plants
A. General Information

1. The 240, 000 species of angiosperms are commonly known as flowering plants. They are the largest single division of plants. Their primary characteristic is flowers. Ecologically, the flowering plants are the most modern and most dominant plant life on earth.

2. The term angiosperm means "seed vessel", referring to the fact that the vessel is the carpel. A carpel is a rolled leaf with seeds on margins. Note, the carpel is part of the pistil of the flower and is technically defined as an ovule containing part of the pistil.

3. The seeds of angiosperms develop from ovules and are part of an ovary that ultimately forms a **fruit**. Angiosperms differ dramatically from gymnosperms because the ovules and seeds are enclosed rather than exposed.

4. Consensus of opinion is that angiosperms are derived from pteridosperm and that the flower is actually a modified stem bearing modified leaves. Supporting this premise is the fact that the most primitive angiosperm flowers have a long receptacle with spirally arranged flower parts that are separate and not differentiated into sepals and petals. Magnolias and buttercups have these primitive flowers.

5. As in gymnosperms, the sporophyte is the dominant generation in angiosperms. The gametophyte generation is small, short lived and attached to the sporophyte.

6. Taxonomically, the angiosperms are divided into two classes, the monocots and dicots.

B. The Female Gametophyte of Flowering Plants

1. The female gametophyte develops from the flower. While the flower is developing in the bud, the diploid **megaspore mother cell** differentiates in the ovule, undergoing meiosis to produce 4 haploid megaspores. Three

degenerate but the 4th undergoes mitosis and enlarges into a cell with 8 haploid nuclei. This 8 haploid nuclei stage represents the embryo sac of the female gametophyte.

2. Of these 8 haploid nuclei in the embryo sac, 1 becomes the **egg cell**, 2 become associated with the egg cell as helper cells or **synergids**, 3 become **antipodal cells** that have no known function and 2 become **polar nuclei**, and remain in the middle of the cell.

3. At the same time, the two outer layers of cells of ovule differentiate to become **integuments** that will later become the **seed coat**. As they develop they leave an opening called a microphyle at one end through which the pollen will migrate to fertilize the egg within.

C. The Male Gametophyte of Flowering Plants

1. The pollen grain represents the male gametophyte of flowering plants. Pollen is produced in the anthers, or male part of the angiosperm flower.

2. Patches of tissue in the anthers that contain diploid **microspore mother cells** undergoes meiosis, producing a tetrad of 4 haploid **microspores** which are the pollen grains. Each microspore nuclei divides to produce a **tube nucleus** and a **generative nucleus.**

3. The generative nucleus will later divide to produce two sperms. The tube nucleus is involved in the growth of the pollen tube towards the micropyle of the embryo sac.

D. Pollination in Angiosperms

1. Pollination is the transfer of the male pollen grains from the anther of the flower to female stigma of the same flower or to a different flower. By comparison, fertilization is the union of sperm and egg which may not occur until days or months after pollination.

    a. **Self Pollination** is the transfer of pollen from the anther to the stigma of the same flower or from one flower to another flower on the same plant.

    b. **Cross Pollination** is the transfer of pollen from one plant to another. Cross pollination increases the genetic variation of offspring.

2. The mode of pollination varies between angiosperm groups but most pollination is brought about by animals, including small birds, bats, rodents, and especially insects such as dipterans (flies), lepidopterans (moths and butterflies), and hymenopterans (bees).

3. Wind pollinated flowers (e.g., grasses) are typically small and often lack or have reduced sepals and petals. The exposed anthers and stigma facilitates pollen transfer.

4. Animal pollinated flowers typically have a reward for their pollinators in the form of nutrients.

5. Bee pollinated flowers reward the bee with a sugary nectar. As the bee visits a flower to feed on the nectar pollen catches on its legs. When the bee visits the next flower, some of the pollen is transferred to the stigma. Bee pollinated flowers are often blue or yellow in color and may have ultraviolet markings that attract the bee to the nectar.

6. Flowers pollinated by flies such as skunk cabbage usually emit smelly odors such as the odor of rotten flesh and are dull red or brown in color, exactly like rotten flesh.

7. Orchid flowers employ many strategies. Some are shaped like female insects, as the male insect tries to mate with the female shaped flower he pollinates it. Other orchid flowers produce **pollinia** or pollen sacs that stick to parts of insects and are carried to the next flower by them. Some orchid flowers dunk insect in a pool of intoxicating fluid. As the insect escapes it pollinates the flower in process.

E. Fertilization in Flowering Plants

1. Pollination involves transfer of the pollen grains to the stigma. Following pollination the pollen grain germinates to produce a pollen tube containing three cells. Two of the cells are **sperm cells** and the third cell becomes the **tube nucleus**.

2. The pollen tube containing the sperm cells and tube nucleus, migrates down through the pistil by enzymatically digesting a pathway through the style of the pistil, eventually reaching the embryo sac containing the eggs which is located at the base of the pistil.

3. Once the pollen tube enters the embryo sac, the tube nucleus disintegrates and a process called **double fertilization** occurs.

    a. One of the sperm cells unite with the egg to form the zygote.

    b. The second sperm cell unites with the two polar nuclei of the embryo sac. These three cells further divide to produce an extensive **endosperm** that will provide nourishment for the germination and growth of the seed.

4. The result of all this is that the ovule has become a seed and the ovary has become a fruit.

5. This process occurs in about 70% of all flowering plants. In the other 30% the endosperm is used as nourishment during the production of the cotyledons.

6. Double fertilization is important because flowering plants can allocate energy for reproduction much more efficiently, i.e., seed and fruit growth occurs only after fertilization, therefore little or no energy is wasted preparing these structures prior to fertilization.

7. This also relates to the specialization of angiosperm flowers, as only pollen that has the correct genetic enzymes can bore its way into the ovule and fertilize the egg within.

F. Apomixis and Parthenocarpy

1. The development of seeds without fertilization is called **apomixis**. Instead, the embryo develops directly from an ovule cell. The seed represents a vegetatively produced (asexually) plant.
2. Plants that develop from ovaries having unfertilized eggs are called **parthenocarpic**. Such fruits are seedless. Seedless oranges, grapes and other varieties of figs and grapes are examples of parthenocarpy.

II. Flowering Plants and Civilization
A. Origin of Cultivated Plants

1. Some important cultivated plants that originated in China or the Orient include: millets, soybeans, bamboo, radish, eggplant, cucumber, some citrus plants, peaches, apricots, walnuts, the persimmon, tea, sugar, cane, and hemp.
2. Cultivated plants that originated in the Indian subcontinent include, rice, sorghum, mung and other beans, gourds, yam, mango, orange, hemp, peppers, gum Arabic, and betel nut.
3. Some cultivated plants that originated in the Indo-Malayan area of Indochina, Malaysia, Java, Borneo, Sumatra and the Philippines include giant bamboo, ginger, banana, breadfruit, candlenut, coconut, clove, nutmeg, Manila hemp, and many tropical fruits.
4. Some cultivated plants that originated in the Central Asiatic area of Northwest India, Afghanistan, and adjacent Soviet Provinces include wheat, garden pea, lentil, mustard, safflower, cotton, garlic, carrot, onion, basil, pear, almond, grape, apple, and other fruits and nuts.
5. Cultivated plants of a Near east Origin such as Asia Minor, Iran, the Transcaucas, and highlands of Turkmenistan include wheat, rye, barley, oats, alfalfa, vetch, anise, poppy, cantaloupe, cabbage, lettuce, fig, pomegranate, cherry and hazelnut.
6. Cultivated plants that originated in areas bordering the Mediterranean Sea include fava beans, clover, flax, black mustard, olive, carob, beet, parsley, leek, chive, savory, celery, parsnip, rhubarb, caraway, thyme, hyssop, lavender, peppermint, sage, rosemary, hop and chufa.
7. Some of the cultivated plants that originated in the Ethiopia and Somaliland area include sesame, garden cress, coffee, okra, indigo, and fenugreek.
8. Some of the cultivated plants that originated in Central America (Southern Mexico, Guatemala, El Salvador, Honduras, Nicaragua, and Costa Rica) include maize, common bean, lima bean, sweet potato, pepper, some cotton varieties, prickly pear, papaya, cashew, cacao, cherry, tomato, and the annatto source of dyes and spices.
9. Some of the cultivated plants that originated in the Highlands of Peru, Ecuador, and Bolivia include potatoes, tomato, pumpkin, marigold, cocaine plant, Egyptian cotton, guava, tobacco, and the quinine tree.

10. Some of the cultivated plants that originated in the Chiloe Island off the coast of Southern Chile include the common whiter or Irish potato, and strawberry.

11. Cultivated plants that have an origin centered in the Brazilian-Paraguay area include manioc (cassava), peanut, passion fruit, pineapple, brazil nut, and the Para rubber tree.

III. The Classes of Flowering Plants
A. General Information

1. The division Anthophyta is subdivided into two classes, the Class Dicotyledonae and the Class Monocotyledonae. These are commonly referred to as the monocots and dicots.

2. Within each classes are a number of orders of plants. Within each order are families of plants.

3. The two classes of flowering plants differ in a number of features including number of food storage organs (the cotyledons), leaf shape, arrangement of vascular bundles, leaf veination, and types of root systems.

B. The Monocots

1. Monocots take their name from the fact that each monocot seed has a single leaf.

2. Flower parts of monocots (sepals, petals, stamens) are 3 or in multiples of 3.

3. Monocot leaves typically have parallel veins.

4. Monocot roots are typically fibrous, e.g., grasses.

5. The vascular bundles are scattered throughout the stem, e.g., corn stem.

6. Monocots are mostly herbaceous plants that lack true secondary growth.

7. The major examples of monocots include the grasses, lilies, orchids, and palms.

C. The Dicots

1. The dicots are so named because they have two seed leaves or cotyledons.

2. Dicots have flower parts that occur in 4 or 5 e.g., 4 stamens, 4 sepals, 4 petals.

3. Dicots leaves have oval, lance like or palmate (shaped like a hand) leaves and a net like pattern of veins in the leaf.

4. Dicots typically have a single taproot which in turn may split into smaller roots and rootlets, all of which ultimately feed into the single taproot. This taproot enables some dicots to obtain water and minerals from great depths in the soil.

5. The vascular bundles of dicots form a ring like structure inside the epidermis. The phloem is the outside of the ring, the xylem is the inside of the ring. The layer of vascular cambium is between the xylem and phloem. In woody dicots, it is the growth of xylem that contributes to most of the increase in the girth, or width of the stem.

6. Many dicots are herbaceous but many species also exhibit woody secondary growth. Almost all of the flowering plants that are large enough to be called trees and shrubs of the world are dicots.
7. Some major examples of dicots include the mustards, mints, flowering shrubs and trees.

Table 23.1 Comparison of dicot and monocot characteristics.

Attribute	Dicot	Monocot
Flowers	4 parted or 5 parted or multiples of 4 or 5 sepals, petals, other floral parts	3 parted or multiples of 3 in sepals , petals, other floral features
Seed Embryo	Two seed leaves (cotyledons)	One seed leaf (cotyledon)
Leaves	Oval leaves	Linear, grass like or lily like
Leaf Veins	Net like patterns	Parallel
Vascular Tissue	Vascular bundles of xylem and phloem arranged in a ring inside stem	Vascular bundles scattered throughout stem
Root Type	Taproot	Fibrous root
Examples	Many weeds, flowering plants, woody trees and shrubs	Grasses, lilies, palms, orchids

IV. Selected Families of Flowering Plants

Families of Dicots

A. Magnolias- Family Magnoliaceae
1. Members of the magnolia family include the magnolia, sweet bay, and tulip tree.
2. This family has large, showy flowers.

B. Buttercups- Family Ranunculaceae
1. Flowers of buttercups have numerous stamens and pistils with petals variable in number. The flower ovary is superior. Most of the family are herbaceous plants.

2. The 1500 species of buttercups are concentrated in North temperate and Arctic regions.

3. Examples include buttercup, columbine, larkspur, peony, hellebore, anemone, monkshood and *Clematis*. Most members of the family are somewhat or slightly poisonous.

C. Laurels- Family Lauraceae

1. Laurel flowers lack petals but the six sepals are sometimes petal like. Stamens occur in three or 4 whorls of three each and the ovary is superior.

2. The 1,000 species are most tropical with aromatic leaves.

3. The family includes many spices such as cinnamon, cassia, camphor, sassafras, and avocados.

D. Barberries- Family Berberidacea

1. The barberry family includes the Japanese and Common Barberry as well as the May Apple.

2. Barberries are widely used as landscape ornamentals, providing a protective thorny hedge.

3. Wild barberry is important as one of the hosts in the complex life cycle of wheat rust.

E. Poppies- Family Papaveraceae

1. The poppies are mostly herbs of temperate and subtropical regions north of the equator.

2. Poppies have a single pistil and numerous stamens. Their rhizomes produce a milky sap.

3. Opium poppies produce opium and opium derivatives such as morphine, codeine, and heroin.

4. This family includes the poppies, bloodroot, prickly poppy and bleeding heart.

F. Pitcher Plants- Family Sarraceniaceae

1. The pitcher plants are members of bog communities. They are best known for their leaf modifications that enable them to trap insects.

2. The leaves of pitcher plants are rolled into a tube, with a lip shaped top. The bottom is filled with water.

3. Glands on the inside of the leaf secrete a nectar like substance to lure insects which become trapped inside and fall into the pool of water and drown.

4. Enzymes secreted in water digest the insect which provides nitrogen and other needed nutrients to the plant in these nutrient poor habitats.

G. Gourds- Family Cucurbitaceae

1. The gourd family includes a number of species that are important vegetables consumed over much of the world.

2. Most gourds are trailing vines with large flowers.

3. Examples of gourds include the watermelon, cantaloupe, cucumber, squash, and pumpkin.

4. The fruit of all gourds is a pepo.

5. Gourds are highly prized for their grotesque shapes and are widely cultivated as household ornamentals.

H. Willows- Family Salicales

1. The willows bear their flowers in long, string like catkins.

2. Willows are important shrubs and trees of a wide variety of habitats, but especially are trees and shrubs of wetlands.

3. Examples of this family include cottonwood, poplars, willows and aspens.

I. Mustards- Family Brassicaceae

1. The 2500 species of mustards or Cruciferae are named because the 4 petals and 4 sepals of each flower are in the form of a cross. Flowers also have 4 nectar glands and 6 stamens.

2. Mustards are the only family of flowering plants that produce **silicles** as fruits.

3. Mustards are fairly common and widely distributed herbs of temperate and cooler regions of the world. They include a large number of vegetables.

4. Some common food mustards include cabbage, cauliflower, Brussels sprouts, broccoli, radish, kohlrabi, turnip, horseradish, watercress, and rutabaga.

J. Roses- Family Rosaceae

1. The 3,000 species in the rose family include trees, herbs and shrubs.

2. The basal parts of the rose flower fuse into cups with petals, sepals and numerous stamens all attached to the rim of the cup.

3. The roses include the stone fruits such as pears, cherries, apricots, peaches, plums. The pome fruits such as apples, loganberries and raspberries are also in this family.

K. Legumes- Family Fabaceae

1. The legumes are the third largest of all of the families of flowering plants with 13,000 species. They are also called the leguminosidae.

2. Legume flowers are either radial or bilateral. The bilateral petals have a keel, with two petals enclosing the pistil, two wing petals and a banner petal. The stamens are fused and form a tube around the ovary.

3. The fruit is a legume.

4. Examples of legumes include peas, beans, lentils, peanuts, alfalfa, sweet clover, licorice, wattle, carob, indigo, logwood, locoweeds, lupines, black locust, sensitive plant.

5. About 90% of legumes exhibit leaf movements as seen in the sensitive plant.

L. Spurges- Family Euphorbiaceae
1. This family is one of the largest. They are mostly tropical and temperate flowering plants.
2. In the spurges, the stamens and pistils are produced as separate flowers. The flowers also lack a corolla making them inconspicuous. The female flower is elevated on stalk with several male flowers arranged around it.
3. Examples of spurges include poinsettia, cassava (farinha), tapioca, para rubber tree, Mexican jumping beans, and crown of thorns plant.

M. Olives- Family Oleaceae
1. The olive family includes the olives as well as the ashes, privet, forsythia and lilac.
2. The olive members of this family have been cultivated for thousands of years for their fruit.
3. Lilacs, forsythia, and privet are landscape ornamentals. The wood of ash tree is valued for its hardness and is used in the manufacture of handles for axes and other implements.

N. Cashews- Family Anacardiceae
1. The cashew family include the cashews and mangos which are valued as food sources.
2. Other interesting cashews include poison ivy and the sumacs.

O. Cactus- Family Cactaceae
1. The 1500 species of cacti are native to the Americans.
2. Cactus flowers have numerous stamens, petals, and sepals. The sepals are colored like the petals and ovary develops into a berry. Cacti have reduced or absent leaves and the stem is armed with thorns.
3. Cacti are widely used as houseplants and ornamentals.
4. The flesh of cacti can be eaten and the cacti pulp is a source of water.
5. The peyote cactus are small and button like with carrot like tap root. They produce several drugs including the powerful hallucinogen mescaline which is used in religious ceremonies.

P. Goosefoot- Family Chenopodiaceae
1. The goosefoot family includes a variety of weedy herbaceous plants such as saltbush.
2. Important food crops from this family include beets, Swiss chard, and spinach.

Q. Beech and Birch Families- Fagaceae (beeches), Betulaceae
1. These families include many important species of trees and shrubs that occur mostly as understory species in woodlands.
2. The beech family include the oaks, American chestnut, and beech.

3. Oaks are prized for their wood which is used in the manufacture of flooring, wooden ships, and furniture. Beechnuts are harvested from beeches.
4. The birch family includes the birches, alders, hornbeams, and hazelnuts.

R. Mints- Family Lamiaceae
1. The 3,000 species of mints have stems that are square in cross section, opposite leaves and bilateral flowers. Mints are also recognized by their distinctive "minty" smell.
2. Mints include rosemary, thyme, sage, oregano, marjoram, basal, lavender, catnip, peppermint, spearmint, horehounds, vinegar weed, salvias, and coleus, menthol produced from mint oil.

S. Nightshades-Family Solanaceae
1. The 3,000 species of nightshades are mostly plants of Latin American tropics.
2. The petals are fused together at their base, the filaments of stamens are fused to the corolla and so appear to be arising from it. The superior ovary develops into a berry or capsule.
3. This is a very familiar family- examples tomato, white potato, eggplant, pepper, tobacco, and petunia.
4. Many of the nightshades produce poisonous drugs (belladonna, atropine, scopolamine, hyoscyanmine), and Jimson weed.

T. Carrots- Family Apiaceae
1. The 2,000 members of the carrot family are found throughout the Northern Hemisphere.
2. Carrot flowers are typically small, numerous, and arranged in umbles e.g., wild carrot or Queen Anne's Lace.
3. Many members of the carrot family are aromatic and include dill, celery, carrot, parsley, caraway, coriander, fennel, anise and parsnip.

U. Pumpkins- Family Cucurbitaceae
1. The 700 species of pumpkins are mostly tropical forms but many species are cultivated in the temperate areas of the world.
2. Pumpkins are mostly prostrate or climbing herbaceous vines with tendrils. The unisexual flowers have fused petals and an inferior ovary with three carpals. Some plants have male and female flowers on the same plant, other species have separate male and female flowers.
3. Examples are squashes, cucumbers, cantaloupes, watermelons, vegetable sponge and gourds.

V. Sunflowers- Family Asteraceae
1. The 20,000 species of asters comprise the largest family of flowering plants. The family is typically called the aster or sunflower family.

2. The individual flowers (florets) are tiny and arranged in compact inflorescence so resemble single flower. The result is a compound flower head (i.e., the typical sunflower or aster flower) in which the central disk flowers are surrounded by a single row of ray flowers.
3. Most of the members of this family are herbaceous weeds such as thistle and chicory.
4. Familiar examples within this family include the sunflowers, daisy, dandelions, lettuce, endive, chicory, Jerusalem artichoke, dahlia, chrysanthemum, marigold, thistle, and yarrow.
5. Endive, lettuce, and artichoke are harvested for foods.
6. The family also contains troublesome weeds such as the goldenrods, dandelions, ragweed, and burdock.

Families of Monocots

A. Grasses- Family Poaceae
1. The grasses are the largest family of flowering plants numbering 80,000 species perhaps more. They along with lilies are monocots.
2. Grasses have a complex and greatly reduced flower.
3. Grasses include the very important group of flowering plants known as the cereals, e.g., wheat, rye, barley, oats, rice, and corn as well as sugar cane, and sorghum.

B. Lilies- Family Liliaceae
1. This family of monocots includes about 2,000 species. They are especially abundant in the tropics and subtropics of the world but there are also a number of temperate species as well.
2. Lily flowers comparatively large (e.g., tiger lilies). Parts of the flower occur in 3's or multiples of 3. The sepals are usually colored the same as petals.
3. The lilies include many species that are prized ornamentals because of their beautiful flowers such as the day lilies, tiger lilies and tulips.
4. The lilies include important useful species such as asparagus, sarsaparilla, squill, meadow saffron, bowstring hemp and Aloe.
5. The onion, leak, and wild garlic are important garnishes.

C. Orchids- Family Orchidaceae
1. The 35,000 species of orchids are especially abundant in the tropics. Many orchids are epiphyte, growing on other trees.
2. Orchid flowers may be exceptionally varied and specialized. Flowers usually have three sepals and 3 petals with the "lip" petal differing from the other two.
3. Many orchids are used as ornamentals, e.g. vanilla.

D. Palms- Family Arecaceae

1. The palms are sometimes placed in the Palmae which is another name for the family.
2. Although, the several hundred species of palms are mostly tropical and subtropical plants they have been widely cultivated as ornamentals.
3. The coconuts and dates are two important food producing members of this family.
4. Other members include the betel nut, date palm, and saw palmetto.

E. Arums- Family Aracea

1. The arums include two members of interest to botanists and wildflower enthusiasts, the skunk cabbage of swamps and other wetlands and the Jack in the pulpit of wet woodlands.
2. Skunk cabbage is the familiar harbingers of spring as they sprout amidst snow and cold of late January and February.

F. Cattails- Family Typhaceae

1. The cattails are ecologically important plants of most temperate wetlands. They are food to a wide variety of mammals and birds.
2. Cattails also bind wetland soils and filter water.

G. Duckweeds- Family Lemnaceae

1. These are the smallest flowering plants in the world. Most are only a few millimeters in size.
2. These small floating plants consist of a leaf like thallus and a few simple roots dangling below.
3. Although they produce flowers, most reproduction is asexual by budding or fragmentation.
4. As their name implies, the duckweeds are important food for ducks and other waterfowl.

Multiple Choice Self-Test

_____ 1. We use this to separate leaves of monocots from dicots: (a) venetation (b) thickness (c) petiole length (d) all of the above.

_____ 2. This floral part may be highly modified to attract insect pollinators: (a) pistil (b) carpel (c) petal (d) stamen (e) ovary (f) all of the above.

_____ 3. The two basic categories of flowering plants are based on: (a) rooting structures (b) pollen (c) seeds (d) stems (e) pollen (f) all of the above.

_____ 4. Angiosperms differ from gymnosperms in having: (a) protected seed (b) dominant sporophyte generation (c) dominant gametophyte (d) xylem and phloem (e) woody tissue in older plants.

_____ 5. The process of pollination involves: (a) pollen transfer from anther to stigma (b) pollen tube (c) pollen tube nucleus (d) all of the above.

_____ 6. Cells that fuse together prior to fertilization? (a) pollen grains (b) sperm (c) polar nuclei (d) antipodals (e) synergids (f) all of the above

_____ 7. Fruits that develop from unfertilized eggs: (a) hybrid (b) decadent (c) homohormal (d) parthenocarpic (e) all of the above.

_____ 8. The 3n tissue found in angiosperms: (a) zygote (b) sperm (c) egg (d) antipodal (e) endosperm (f) antipodal (g) synergid.

_____ 9. Occurrence of both male and female flowers on a plant: (a) monoecious (b) dioecious (c) heterosexual (d) bisexual (e) asexual.

_____10. Primitive flowers: (a) show radial symmetry (b) show mostly fusion of petals (c) lack petals or sepals (d) have only petals and sepals.

_____11. The most highly modified part of a flower for attracting insects and other pollinators: (a) petals (b) sepals (c) nectary (d) stamens (e) ovaries.

_____12. Factor we used to identify and categorize the major groups of flowers: (a) petals (b) sepals (c) carpels (d) seeds (e) pollen (f) stamens.

_____13. To differentiate a monocot leaf from a dicot leaf: (a) look at its venation (b) count its chromosomes (c) see if it has any DNA (d) all of the above.

_____14. Important evolutionary trends in angiosperms and other vascular plants: (a) complex vascular systems (b) smaller gametophyte (c) the development of seeds (d) heterospory (e) all of the above.

Matching Self-Test

_____ 1. Pollen is produced in   a. anthers
_____ 2. Pollen is deposited in   b. ovary
_____ 3. Eggs are produced in   c. parthenocarpic
_____ 4. Seeds are produced in   d. apomixes
_____ 5. Plants that develop from unfertilized eggs   e. stigma
.

Visual Self-Test

First read the section that describes the life cycle of a typical flowering plant in your book and lab manual. Then, without the aid of references, label all of the parts, structures, and events in this life cycle.

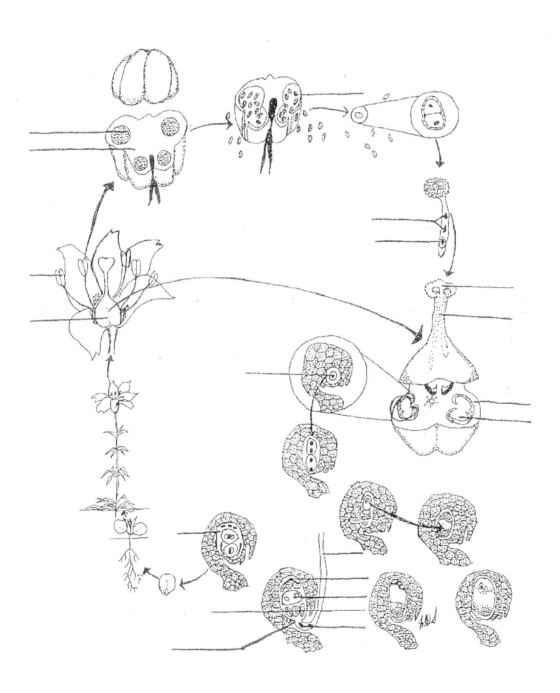

Chapter 24 Foods and Medicines from Plants

I. Food and Agriculture
A. The First Farmers
    1. Prior to extensive farming humans lived as hunter-gathers.
          a. They gathered roots, berries and other fruits.
          b. They hunted small animals with stones and clubs.
    2. The discovery of agriculture provided more stable food supply and
        also larger amounts of food. Fewer people needed to work
        at obtaining sufficient food for all.
    3. Since fewer people were needed to produce food, more people could
        be employed in other activities.
    4. Gave rise to trades such as full-time shepards, builders, priests,
        entertainers.

B. Origins and Worldwide Introduction of Food Plants
    1. Food plants were originally wild plants that had been harvested such as carrots
        pumpkins, squash, corn.
    2. The first agriculture really began in the Fertile Crescent of the Middle East
        with wheat and barley crops.
    3. Agriculture spread throughout the world with the discovery and colonization
        of the New World and Australia.
          a. Each group of pioneers brought their own food crops, fruits,
            vegetables, and pasture grasses.
          b. So the basic crops soon became spread throughout the world.

C. Early Centers of Agriculture
    1. Fertile Crescent of the Middle East, or Near East. The Egyptians, Sumarians,
        Babylonians, and other peoples grew wheat, barley, lentil, pea, and
        Einkorn to feed themselves and their flocks of sheep, goats, and cattle.
    2. Southern and central China agriculture concentrated on crops of rice, soybean,
        millet, taro, and peas.
    3. Beginning about 5000 years ago, MesoAmerican Native Peoples grew crops of
        squash, maize, beans, and cotton.

II. Contributions of Crops as Food for Humans
A. The Primary Food Crops
    1. Plants provide 80% of calories of all calories consumed by humans

2. Three most important crops are all grains, rice, wheat, and corn.
3. Other important crops include potatoes, sweet potatoes, and manioc, sugar cane and sugar beets, barley, sorghum, soybeans, bananas, and yams.

B. The Cereal Food Crops

1. Oats are comprised of about 20% protein 10% unsaturated oils. Oats are a common ingredient in cereal grain breads and pastries, porridge, oatmeal cookies and oatmeal.
2. Barley is used in whole grain breads and baked goods. It is feed for livestock Barley is also important in production of hops to make beer.
3. Rye grain is valued for its mineral and fiber content. Rye is used in preparation of alcoholic beverages.
4. Millets are grain crops of semiarid and arid habitats. Produces a flat bread.
5. Sorghum is the staple food for many African natives. Some additional products from sorghum include beer and bread.
6. Flax is used for plant fibers for weaving of linen cloth.
7. Wheat, Corn, and Rice are the three most important cereal crops

C. The Importance of Wheat

1. Wheat seeds contain gluten, used to hold bread together.
   a. There are two types: bread wheat and durum wheat.
   b. 90% is bread wheat a.k.a. spring wheat; two kinds: hard wheat (breads) and soft wheat (pastries, cakes, cookies, biscuits).
   c. Durum wheat (macaroni wheat) is used in preparation of noodles for spaghetti, macaroni and lasagna.

D. The Importance of Corn

1. This New World plant is also called maize or Indian corn.
2. There are three types of corn: field corn, sweet corn, and popcorn.
   a. Field corn (dent corn) grown for livestock feed, corn meal, corn syrup and gasohol.
   b. Sweet corn- high in sugar and lower starch concentration
   c. Baby corn contains mostly water
   d. 50% of world's corn is grown in the Corn Belt of the United States. Other areas include Europe and Asia.

E. The Importance of Rice

1. Rice is the staple food crop for 1.6-2 billion people. Most of the peoples of India and Southeast Asia depend on rice as their staple food crop.
2. It is a grass of hot rainy tropics and subtropics.
3. Cultivation centers include India, Southeast Asia, Japan and Philippines.

III. The Legumes as Food Crops
A. The Importance of Legumes

1. Legumes rank second in importance to cereals as food crops of humans.
   a. Legumes are high in starches (40-90%) and proteins (20-40%)

   b. Legumes are excellent sources of plant oils and minerals (calcium, magnesium, iron, phosphorous, zinc, copper, potassium.
   c. Because their root nodules contain nitrogen fixing bacteria legumes are used as a green manure to improve soil fertility.
2. Major legume crops include beans, peas and peanuts.
3. Beans or Pulses (beans, fava beans, peas, chickpeas, lentils).
   a. Pulses are comprised of 17-31% proteins
   b. The Common French Bean is the most widely cultivated pulse crop; this is the bean of baked beans, kidney beans, navy and pinto beans.
   c. The Faba bean, also called the broad bean, Windsor bean, field bean, and horse bean, is cultivated in 50 countries.
   d. The Lima bean, also called the butter bean or Madagascar bean has a high protein and carbohydrate content and is a favorite in succotash and other vegetable dishes.
4. Peas are the second most important legume crop
   a. Peas are a nutritious food containing 18-23% protein and 60% carbohydrates; eaten fresh, cooked, canned, or frozen.
5. The Chick pea is the third important pulse crop It is an important crop in Middle East, Mediterranean region and India.
6. Lentils are widely cultivated in India, Spain, Ethiopia, Syria and Turkey. They are an important snack food are used in soups, ground into flour, or used to make breads and pastries.
7. The Oilseeds are the source of Soya, spices, sprouts, and leaves used in cooking.
   a. Soybeans major crop source is in Asia; used for soups, tofu, soymilk, cheeses, yogurt and other dairy products.
   b. Oilseed spices include tamarind and fenugreek.
8. The peanuts are also called ground nuts, monkey nuts, or goobers. They are rich in protein (25-30%) and plant oils (45-50%)
   a. Also rich in oleic and linoleic acids
   b Used to make peanut butter and rest for snacks and candies
   c. Peanuts are also harvested for peanut oil (margarine, salad dressing) and remainder for livestock feed.
9. Carob is used in making cookies, bread, cakes, and carob chocolate.

IV. The Vegetable Food Crops
A. Underground Stem, Root, and Tuber Food Crops

1. Foods commonly called vegetables include plant stems (potatoes), roots, (cassava) and leaves (cabbage).
2. Families of vegetables include Apiaceae family (carrots and parsnips), Solanaceae family (tomato, potato) and Cruciferae family (turnip, cabbage, kale).
3. The root vegetables are crops in which the roots are harvested.
   a. Carrots are one of the most important root vegetables. They can be eaten raw, cooked or processed in juice. Carrots are valued for vitamin A content, high in carotenes.
   b. Parsnips harvested for value of their tap roots, leaves are used to garnish foods and parsnip wine.
4. Potatoes are the most important tuber crop. Potato harvest exceeds that of cereal crops in many areas of the world.
   a. Potatoes grow well in cool and wet locations.
   b. Potatoes consist of 78% water; rich in carbohydrates and low in fat and protein.
5. The sweet potato is widely cultivated in Asia and Africa.
   a. Sweet Potato is not related to true potatoes, rather, it is in the Convolvulacea family which includes the morning glories.
   b. Sweet Potato is actually a modified root while potatoes are a true tuber.
6. Cassava root (manioc) is a tropical tuber; dietary staple; can be baked into a type of bread or used as an additive or thickener in soups and sauces.
7. Salad Roots include two types: the radishes and the beetroots
   a. Radishes are a member of the crucifer or mustard family; harvested for their fleshy, edible bulb like root. Varieties include western radishes (salad component), oriental radishes (flavorful additions to soups/sauces and rat tailed radishes of Asia.
   b. Beetroots are high in sugars and pigments. They are used to make borsch soups of Russia and Poland.

B. Leafy, Stem, and Flower Vegetables Food Crops

1. Leafy vegetables are common food crops.
2. Leaves of onions (chives, leeks, garlic) are used as food crops and medicines.
   a. Important herbs used in treatment of intestinal worms.
   b. Also used to treat high blood pressure, also fungal and bacterial infections.
   c. Onions can be eaten fresh, canned, frozen, roasted or pickled.
   d. Onions are desirable flavoring agents in soups, salads, sauces

and preparation of poultry, fishes and prepared dishes.

3. Spinach is a rather "unpopular" leafy vegetable valued for vitamin content (B, C, E), carotenes and minerals. Can be eaten fresh or cooked or mixed in salads.

4. The cabbages (wild, head, red, spring) are a common salad ingredient and used to make sauerkraut.

5. The leaf stalk or petiole of the celery plant is used for food, also for medicinal plant to reduce both excess gas and arthritis. Celery leaves are used to sweeten blood and cure scurvy if eaten in spring. Celery is also a common leaf in salads and soups.

6. Lettuce is a salad vegetable. It contains minerals (potassium), vitamin B carotene and some vitamin E and C.

7. Asparagus stalks are cooked and served with butter or white sauce.

8. Bamboo shoots are stem vegetables prepared by boiling then eaten raw or canned.

9 Rhubarb stems used in rhubarb pies, preserves, cookies and rhubarb wine.

10. Flowering heads or buds of some plants are also food crops.

     a. Artichokes or (globe artichoke), a perennial member of the compositae family-- globular flower heads are harvested.

     b. The dense buds of brussels sprouts resemble cabbages.

     c. The edible part of broccoli are flower heads.

     d. Cauliflower is a member of the Brassica group. Its edible portion is the swollen flower head which is borne on a single stem.

11. Fruits of Plants are valuable food crops.

     a. Cucumber like plants, edible portion is a fruit eaten raw or cooked; 2% carbohydrates, some vitamin C and B and carotenes

     b. Gherkins are small cucumber; picked fresh and pickled

     c. Pumpkins are actually a Latin American fruit; associated with Halloween; pie consumed throughout year, raw, roasted or cooked. Mostly water with small amounts of starches, sugars, vitamins, minerals, and carotene. Squashes are also members of this group.

C. Vegetable Oils as Food Crops

1. Plant oils can be extracted from seeds and fruits by pressing plant parts.

     a. Pressing produces a material called press cake which is rich in protein and used as animal feed

     b. Plant oils are used in cooking, salad dressings, and the manufacture of margarine.

2. Sunflowers of the genus *Helianthus* yield 40% polyunsaturated oil, 20%

protein. They are used as a cooking oil and also garnish salads. Also used as an industrial lubricant, been tested for use as a biofuel.

3. Other popular plant oils include olive, palm, corn, safflower, soya bean oils

4. Soya bean oils are from seeds which have a high protein content (30-50%) also contain 15-25% oil in the form of linoleic and oleic acids.

5. Cotton seed oil is pressed from seed after cotton fiber removed. This oil used mostly for cooking.

D. Fruits as Food Crops

1. Tropical fruits include pineapples, mangoes, papaya, breadfruit, avocado and plantains.

2. Pineapples are originally from tropical South America. The fruit is consumed fresh or frozen, canned or processed pineapple juice. Fresh pineapple is high vitamin content; dried pineapple has 70% sugar content

    a. Pineapples can be distilled to produce alcohol and fermented to produce vinegar.

3. Mangoes are originally from Himalayas of India and Burma. The fruit is high in vitamin C and eaten fresh, canned, dried or pulped for juices, jellies, jams, and deserts.

4. Papaya fruit is used as a fresh or dried fruit, salads, ice creams, jams and jellies

    a. good source of sugars, vitamin C and carotenes.

    b. enzyme papain is extracted and used as a meat tenderizer.

5. Breadfruit is a tropical tree of the Pacific, a staple of Pacific islanders.

6. Avocado pear is a tall evergreen tree native to Central America. Also called avocados, this popular fruit is often eaten in salads and used as an ingredient in desserts and salad dishes. Avocado oils are used as a scent in the manufacture of some shampoos and cosmetics.

7. Plantains are a staple food in Africa and Latin America. They are eaten fresh fried, baked, or roasted. Important because they consist of 20% sugars and large amounts of vitamin C and potassium.

    a. good sources of vitamins B, C, E, minerals calcium, iron, potassium and malic and citric acids.

8. Fruits of the Family Rosaceae includes apples, cherries, plums, strawberries pears.

    a. apples: 7000 varieties, 100 kinds grown commercially; good source of sugars, used as snack foods and ingredients in pies, jams and jellies. Fruit of apple is a pome.

    b. pears: 5000 cultivars, 20 species; the fruit of pears is a pome.

9. Many other fruits include blackberry, boysenberry, raspberry, wineberry olives, figs, pomegranates, and dates.

E. Nuts and Nut-like Food Crops

1. Nuts are enclosed in a hard, protective, outer shell which must be discarded to

obtain the kernel. Most nuts are cooked and then eaten. Important ingredients in prepared dishes, ice creams and flavorings. They are also a popular snack food.

2. Examples of nuts include Peanuts, Walnuts, Pecans, Pistachios, Almonds, Brazil nuts, and cashews.

3. True nuts include hickory nuts, Persian or common walnuts. Nuts are valued for their high protein and oil content. They are consumed canned, fresh or used as ingredient in pastries, confectionaries and ice creams

    a. Kernels of most nuts are rich in vitamin B, E, and C.

    b. Shells are ground into flour used in plastic industry.

    c. Oils from nuts are used as ingredients in preparation of paints.

4. Coconut meat is rich in carbohydrates, fats, and proteins. It is eaten fresh or dried to produce copra.

    a. Coconut oil is used in soaps, margarine, cosmetics and confectionaries.

    b. Coconut milk different from coconut water which contains water, sugar, vitamins and minerals.

    c. Coconut leaves are woven into thatch roofs, shells form drinking utensils.

    d. Coconut fibers tied into baskets and trunks carved into dugouts.

F. Spices and Flavorings for Food

1. Spices include white and black peppers, chili, paprika, mustards, cloves, and allspice.

    a. Cloves are the dried, unopened flower buds of evergreen tree

    b. Cloves are spicy flavorings for sauces, pickles, hams, apple cider, and other food and beverages.

    c. An oil extract is used as food and beverage flavoring as well as perfume.

    d. Saffron is the most expensive spice. It takes 70,000 dried saffron flowers to produce a pound of saffron spice. Products include food coloring agents, oils.

2. Flavorings include nutmeg, cinnamon, vanilla, and ginger.

    a. Ginger is used as medicine by India and China.

    b. It is the ground root of rhizome plant used in syrups, sauces, powders, and production of ginger beer.

3. Liquorices come from the roots of a wild perennial of pea family. Must grow 3-5 years before its roots can be harvested.

G. Herbs for Food and Flavorings
1. Herbs were long used in burial and preservation practices.
2. Now mostly used as flavorings in cooking and preparation.
3. Examples of herbs include mints such as rosemary, thyme, basil, lemon balm, dill, fennel, coriander, caraway, anise,
   a. Flavorings for meat, poultry and fish, soups, sauces and salads.
   b. Oils for perfume and cosmetic production.

H. Sugar Crops For Foods and Flavorings
1. Sugar crops are harvested plant sugars such as glucose, fructose, sucrose, and maltose.
2. Sugar crops harvested from sugar cane, sugar beets, and sugar maple (maple syrup).

I. Food From Palms and Cycads
1. Sago Palms produce starches used in breads or stuffing.
   a. Starchy additive to soups and stews. Starch produced is boiled, dried, roasted or fried.
   b. Pearl sago made, used in puddings and pastries.
2. Other palms provide sugary sweeteners, beverages, palm wine, palm oil.
3. Cycads produce pithy starch which is used as paste for bread and soups.

V. Masticatories
A. Gums for chewing and Flavoring.
1. Chewing gum is
   a. chewed but not swallowed
   b. made from dried latex from bark of tropical sapodilla tree
2. Betel nuts
   a. derived from betel palm tree
   b. chewed or sliced into strips
3. Cola
   a. chewed like betel nuts or chewing gum
   b. flavoring in beverages
   c. stimulant because of caffeine content

VI. Beverages
A. Caffeine Beverages
1. Examples include tea, coffee, chocolate, and cocoa.
2. Made from leaves (tea) or nuts.
3. Drink flavorings include lemonade, lime, orange, raspberry, sarsaparilla, birch, chicory, and dandelion.

4. Drinks are made from distilled plant products. Examples include wines, beer, sake, mead, gin, whisky, rum, and vodka..

VII. Narcotics
A. Categories of Narcotics
1. There are three categories of narcotics: stimulants, hallucinogens, and depressants.
2. Stimulants are exemplified by diet pills. They excite nervous system, reduce fatigue and generally increase levels of activity.
3. Hallucinogens include opium, heroin, morphine. They are mind altering

 drugs that mostly induce a dream like state of euphoria and/or an unreal feelings of well being.
4. Depressants are so called because they dull mental activity and slow the thought processes.
5. Pain Killers include opium, papaverine, and noscapine.
6. Nonaddictive alkaloids include codeine- found in cough syrups, hypnotics, analgesics and papaverine which relieves muscle spasms.
7. Stress relieve is obtained from cocaine, marijuana, and tobacco.

B. Active Components of Plant Medicines
1. Alkaloids have bitter taste, are extracted from coffee family (Rubiaceae), the nightshade family (Solanaceae) and legume family (Fabaceae).
2. Examples of alkaloids include ephedrine, morphine, caffeine, cocaine, nicotine
   a. most act as stimulants.
3. Glycosides consist of sugar molecule bound to another molecule such as a Glucose bound to fatty acid or protein.
4. Glycoside examples include steroids and saponins.

C. Examples of Plant Medicines
1. Aspirin is an analgesic (pain killer). It is derived from bark of willow. It has 3 important medical properties, analgesic (pain killer), antipyretic (fever reducing drug) and anti-inflamatory.
   a. salicylic acid important ingredient.
   b. use by Greeks and Romans to treat aches and pains, and gout.
   c. reduces heart attacks and strokes.
   d. reduction of colon cancer.
2. Quinine is an alkaloid extract from Fever Bark Tree. Used for centuries by Incas to cure malaria. Quinine destroys protozoan parasites in the blood.
3. Reserpine is an extract from roots of evergreen shrub called snakeroot.
   a. use to cure snake bites and insect stings.
   b. may help cure mental illness.
   c. reduce anxiety and blood pressure.

d. acts as sedative to calm central nervous system.
4. Digitalis is a glycoside extracted from foxglove. It is important in the treatments of dropsy (form of edema or bloating).
    a. digitoxin and digoxin use for treatment of heart conditions.
    b. also use to treat congestive heart failure, reduce or eliminate atrial arrhythmias.
5. Cortisones from yams are an excellent source of natural cortisone steroids for treatment of inflammation, Addison's Disease, bursitis, gout, bowel disease, skin diseases, rheumatoid arthritis
6. Atropine is derived from roots and leaves of belladonna plant and is a source of hyoscyamine and scopolamine. Atropine is a cardiac stimulant, treatment for certain kinds of organic poisoning, and use to dilate pupils
7. Ginseng Acids are an extract from roots of ginseng plant. They are used to improve mental power and reduce fatigue. Ingredients- panax acid and panaxin.

D. Examples of Popular Herbal Medicines
1. Garlic is a member of the onion family used to lessen cholesterol levels, reduce heart disease and cancer, dilate blood vessels and reduce blood clots.
2. Ginkgo extract reduces onset of Alzheimer's disease, enhances memory in all ages, and eliminates ringing in the ears.
3. Horse Chestnut seeds are poisonous. They are used to reduce hemorrhoids, strengthen walls of capillary blood vessels, and reduce intensity and discomfort of varicose veins.
4. Tablets of Saw Palmetto have been used to relieve swollen prostate or benign prostatic hyperplasia.
5. The pungent aromatic oil extract of Eucalyptus leaves is used as an antiseptic, for treatment of bronchial congestion, asthma, and as an ingredient in cough syrup and cough drops.
6. Echinacea or Coneflower was used by Plain Indians of North America to treat snakebites and toothaches. Folks still find it useful as antibiotic, antiseptic, drug to restore health and happiness, alleviate flu and cold symptoms.
7. Bloodroot is a member of poppy family. It is used as antiplague mouthwash and emetic, and to relieve congestion cause by flu and colds.
8. Black Cohosh. This member of the buttercup family is used for a mild sedative for treatments of menopause, especially to alleviate menstrual cramps.
9. Witch Hazel is a shrub. The alcohol or water based extract is widely used as in skin applications, mostly as a topical antiseptic and astringent.
10. Feverfew is also known as Bachelor's button. It is used to cure fever or at least reduce the intensity of fever. Native Americans also used it to

reduce tension, stop diarrhea and as a treatment for colds.
11. Culver's Root is a member of the snapdragon family. It is used for a blood cleanser and body purifier. The Puritans believed that it cured tuberculosis but this has been found not to be true.
12. Boneset provides a hot tea for break bone fever, relieves fever, and is also a laxative and diuretic.

Concepts Self-Test

1. Make a list of natural foods that are the source of natural medicines.

2. How does the old cliché (old saying) "there can be too much of a good thing" apply to the use of narcotics as medicines?

3. Do spices and flavorings contribute any food or nutrition value for us or do they just make food taste good?

4. From a nutritional standpoint, what are the most valuable plant foods.

5. The Green Revolution and Genetic Breeding of Plants discussed in earlier chapters are concentrating on what food groups and why?